10-

IT HAPPENED
IN DETROIT

IT *Happened* IN DETROIT

by H. C. L. JACKSON

Detroit CONJURE HOUSE *1947*

The stories and sketches in IT HAPPENED IN DETROIT
are reprinted by permission from The Detroit News
column LISTENING IN ON DETROIT

PRINTED IN THE UNITED STATES OF AMERICA

DEDICATION

This book is gratefully dedicated to the Feature Department of The Detroit News—the friends who so frequently have come to the aid of a discouraged columnist:

DOROTHEA RYAN	BEVERLY BERTRAND
RAY S. AYER	PAUL D. AIRD
E. J. BECK	CECIL BETRON
RUSSELL GORE	W. M. PARK

INTRODUCTION

Detroit must be a grim city, outlanders feel. Strikes, race riots, the clatter and clang of the assembly line, the heat of the forge . . . these are the mental pictures evoked by the name, Detroit, in the minds of people who live elsewhere.

No city in the world is better known, as those who have traveled extensively will testify. But probably no city has ever been more misunderstood.

Most Detroiters are decent and friendly and many levels removed from the headlines. They're pleasant folk, devoted to their families, and interested primarily in living well, laughing often, and loving much.

Everyday on the back page of "The Detroit News" a master story-teller reveals the true Detroit. To an intensely loyal audience of readers he holds up a bright mirror of their daily lives. In this mirror they see themselves—getting along together and striving to do the right thing.

As a chronicler of human reactions and as an interpreter of human nature, H. C. L. Jackson has few peers. Those of us who try to explain what our city is really like to people who know Detroit only by hearsay have often wished they could read some of Jackson's columns.

And now they can. In this book are gathered more than 200 of his vignettes, chosen from his daily output of the last year. Any soul anywhere in the world, who has a heart, will find these tales to be sheer delight. In them he'll recognize his mother-in-law, his neighbor's dog, the sons he raised, and the boys at the office.

The characters in these anecdotes are Detroiters, of course. But they're *real people,* and they comprise the solid core of a great and human city.

W. S. Gilmore,
Editor
The Detroit News

CONTENTS

IT HAPPENED IN DETROIT

'MICKEY' MOVED IN . . .

When Doctor Van was a boy, he could not keep dogs. Please understand—he could have dogs but he could not keep them—each one of them was killed.

The time came when he decided that he could stand no longer the very special anguish that comes to a boy whose dog has died, and the Doctor decided that never again would he have a dog:

Never again would he undergo the horror of the death of his last dog—the despairing, pain-packed yelp as he was killed by a car. So—

The years unfurled their length, and the Doctor kept to his determination, until:

A few months ago, his married daughter had to move to an apartment in Washington, D. C., and that left her with the problem of what to do with her Airedale, "Mickey."

"Dad," she said, one evening, "as a special favor, won't you take Mickey? I don't want to give him to a stranger, and—"

Doctor Van set his jaw. "You know how I have felt about dogs for years," he said, and then, he saw his daughter's eyes, and:

"Oh, well," he grumphed, "if you'll feel any better about it, I'll let your dog sleep in our kitchen. But mind you!" (firmness there) "that's all. He's your dog, and this is only as a favor to you."

And thus it came about that Mickey moved into the Doctor's

kitchen, nights. Daytimes, he was out romping in the yard, and forming doggish friendships up and down the street.

His particular pal turned out to be a nondescript little character, product of a whole procession of mesalliances, who looked a good deal like a floor-mop on limber legs, and answered to the name of "Daisy," if she answered:

Usually, though she didn't answer.

Generally, if a human spoke to her, she went kiting away: sure proof that somewhere in her background had been brutality. Well—

Mickey, as we have said, was given kitchen privileges at night but, if you know dogs, and smart dogs, you will not be surprised at the aftermath:

One evening, when the Doctor was dead-tired, slumped in his chair in the living room, and his wife well asleep upstairs, there came a creak of a swing door, and out of the kitchen padded Mickey, to sprawl at the Doctor's feet, in silence:

In a restful, a therapeutic silence; the healing silence that a good dog knows how to give. And—

It wasn't long after that, before Mickey had the run of the house.

By the time last September came around, Mickey wasn't sleeping in the kitchen any more. He was sleeping on a special rug at the foot of the Doctor's bed—sleeping when the Doctor was home, prowling restlessly about during the long hours when the Doctor's profession kept him away. And then:

Mickey developed sore eyes. The Doctor privately thought he'd caught them from that Daisy.

The Doctor harrumphed and grumbled a little, and proceeded to cure Mickey of those sore eyes.

And when, a couple of weeks later, Mickey's coat began to fall out, the Doctor went to work on that. And again he effected a cure.

But both of those were minor matters compared to what happened to Mickey a month ago. He caught pneumonia.

The Doctor treated him with all the care he could have given a human being. And that is the reason why Mickey came through with flaunting banners, beginning with the day when his crisis passed and he thumped a weak but thankful tail when the Doctor went down to his basement box to see him. So:

It wasn't long before Mickey was outdoors again, a bouncing ball of energy; playing, happy, zestful. And then came yesterday morning:

The Doctor had just walked out the front door when he heard it—that despairing pain-packed yelp of agony; that cry that whisked him back across the bitter years to when he had heard it last—when his dog had been killed by a car.

The Doctor was down the steps and to the curb before he realized it was not Mickey who had been killed.

Out on the icy street lay the body of Daisy, Mickey's draggled playmate. As the Doctor stood there, his heart lifting in guilty thankfulness, a brown flash went past him—Mickey.

Mickey spurted out into the street, with never a glance at the cars that were coming on.

He grabbed Daisy's body by the scruff of the neck and dragged her over and laid her at the Doctor's feet.

THE STAIRS HE HAD CLIMBED

The attorney said: "I suppose the reason it struck me so hard is because I've been in so many sorts of wedding parties—

"Enough so I've come to sense how blatant a wedding can be—or how spiritual.

"The other afternoon, around 4:10 o'clock, with the offices in the County Building closing at 4:30, I got on an elevator and heard the operator ask: 'Do you want to apply for a marriage license on the second floor, or go to the third floor for a waiver?'

"I looked, and there stood a tall young flight officer, leaning on a cane. With him was a tall American girl, no, I want to change that—young woman. And the officer said: 'We want a waiver.'

"I don't know why I pushed in, but I said: 'You come with me and we'll get it fixed up.'

"And, although it was almost closing time, Probate Court did fix it up, and we went back to the County Clerk's office for the license.

"It was 4:30, but the clerks took one look at that young fellow with his cane and the ribbons on his tunic and at the young woman, and they went out of their way to see they got their license. I guess everyone suspected that officer had an artificial leg. Well—"

The attorney went on: "When they told me they wanted to have a civil ceremony right away, I said maybe I could find a judge, so I told them to come up in the elevator and ran up the stairs looking for Judge Jimmy Sexton and, I found him.

"He said he'd be glad to marry them, and as we were talking, the young woman came up the stairs, breathless. She said the back elevator wasn't running. 'And,' she said, 'he's coming up the stairs!'

"I went to the head of that big flight of yellow marble and there he was, coming up—inching up. . . .

"The first thing I noticed was what a tough time he was having. I noticed the set of his jaw. I noticed the way he looked up at the young woman beside me, and then began fighting those stairs again. I started down to help him, but the young woman said softly:

" 'Don't help him. Let him do it for himself.' And she added: 'He's a double amputee.' "

The attorney said: "He made the top of those stairs with his chin up and his breathing controlled, and we went into the Judge's office—

"Just an office, you understand, where a hurried wedding was going to take place. No vaulted church; no flowers; no music; just two young folks in a Judge's office wanting to be married quick, so he could go back to the hospital in Battle Creek.

"And when they stood in front of the Judge's desk, I found myself ranging behind the groom, that tall lad on two Government legs.

"As the Judge started to read the service, that officer did something I didn't understand for a few moments:

"He passed his cane back to me. And what a beating that cane had taken. The handle was worn and tired. Yes, he passed it back to me and suddenly I knew—he wanted to go through that service on his own two feet, or as near his own feet as he ever will have again, without being propped up.

"He stood there, square-shouldered, as the Judge read on. But I forgot him, because I was looking at the young woman's face—there are lots of words in the English language. I began trying to find the one that would describe her expression, with the inner beauty shining through. And then I had the word. Her face was—serene."

The attorney said: "Her face was so serene that I realized this was a noble wedding. With that face in the room there was no need for soft organ music, for flowers, for high vaulted church.

"When they exchanged their vows, they turned to each other, as naturally as flowers turn to the light, and spoke them into each other's eyes.

"These two young people, talking to each other out of their hearts and hopes. . . .

"After the service, I took them down in the front elevator, and they flagged a taxi, and went away. Back to Battle Creek. But before they left, I couldn't help asking the girl if she was a Battle Creek girl.

" 'Oh, no,' she said, 'I'm from Ohio. I've only been in Battle Creek since they brought'—and her eyes shone up at that tall young man with his cane—'since they brought My Husband back from overseas two years ago.'

"Then they thanked me, and were gone.

"And I stood at the curb and thought about all the stairs he's climbed—all the stairs—up from helplessness, with her always standing at the top, confident, proud, and saying:

" 'Don't help him. Let him do it for himself. . . .' "

HOUSE PLANTS ARE ELEPHANTS

When next the circus comes to town, we are going to say a flat "No" to any free-ticket offer, because we are in perfect training to get into the big-top by the time-honored system of toting buckets of water to the elephants.

This is because Mrs. Mama is now in Washington, D. C., looking at the cherry and orange blossoms, and we are vice-president in charge of a flock of house-plants that drink so much we are going to call in Alcoholics Anonymous.

"There really isn't much housework to do," sighed Mrs. Mama when she decided to go to Joe O'Connor's wedding. "I've cleaned and dusted and the refrigerator is crammed with food and you have Seventeen to help you—"

"The only thing I'm worrying about are my plants. Do you think you can water them—especially my African violet?"

"Of course I can," we snorted in a trumpeting masculine way. "I am very Handy around the House."

"Mmmm," said Mrs. Mama and Son Seventeen, looking out a window, casually crossed his fingers. Well—

The moment Mrs. Mama was on her way Wednesday morning, Seventeen inquired: "What're we going to have for dinner?"

We took a quick peek up Church road to be sure Mrs. Mama was out of sight. We hissed:

"You and I are going out for dinner."

Seventeen looked nervous. Said he: "She won't like that. She left a schedule of what we've got to eat before it spoils."

"I washed the dishes Monday night and Tuesday night, while she was making up her mind," we observed grimly. "If we eat at home tonight, you'll wash the dishes."

"Where are we going to eat?" asked Seventeen.

We came home from Joey's Stables in a particularly pleasant mood because:

We'd given Seventeen who is at times critical of our brand of humor, an actual grin by telling him about the man the Draft Board put in the cavalry solely because he'd said he'd been working at Joey's Stables.

Entering the house, we said, briskly: "And now, young man, you and I will do a little housekeeping."

"Gosh," said Seventeen, "I wish I could, but I've got to work."

"You mean you're going to study," we quavered.

"Not exactly," he responded. "I've got to practice for being in the orchestra for the Variety Show, Friday and Saturday nights. Frank Jewell and I are the Trumpets."

"Oh, yes," we sniggered, remembering that Ma Gail had said that Frank and Seventeen sit next to each other and each furtively keeps an eye on the other's trumpet to see which key he has pushed down. Well—

Seventeen produced the trumpet, put a mute on it, and soon the house was normally full of expiring tomcats and one baby with the croup.

We hitched up our pants and looked around the living room. Now—

We don't know how it is with other husbands, but the minute our Mrs. Mama is away, the house is no longer a home: It is just a jumble of ill-tempered inanimate objects waiting for us to take our eye off them so they can do something cussed.

Refrigerators, stoves, faucets, water heaters, dishes, et al, don't like men. As to furniture! Why, the dingbusted stuff just waits around for a chance to do him dirt and, while waiting, in some incomprehensible way, gives birth to rolls of lint.

With such thoughts in mind we looked at Mrs. Mama's list of what to do. Top priority said "Water the plants."

We started watering—12 in the kitchen, including a wild strawberry with whiskers like a Mandarin. Seven in the dining room, counting a great big pot of mother-in-law's tongues, and they must all have been dipsomaniacs.

Five in the living room, if you count a transient—a slick-leafed affair that will leave us when it grows up to go and stand in the linoleumed lobby of a traveling man's hotel and thrive on stale cigar smoke.

Yes, we watered, and we watered. We wouldn't have believed those plants could take that many gallons. By the time we'd made mud-pies of the tops of the earth in those flower-pots, we were so round-shouldered we staggered up to bed, to be lulled to sleep to that trumpet's interpretation of "Oklahoma," if it wasn't "Abide With Me." To sleep, did we say? Yes, and to dream, of insatiable plants with trunks like elephants. Dreams that came with us to the office and—

Chrimus Jehu! We've just remembered something! We were supposed to water that African violet at the bottom. We watered the top. We'll never dare go home again. We'll bet we drowned the damn thing.

DESCRIPTION OF A BOY

It was back in November that we told, over the radio, the description of a boy read by the Reverend Leo F. Fahey, director of vocations, of Natchez, Miss., at a regional meeting on vocations held in New Orleans.

There have been a lot of requests for reprints of that description, so herewith is that whimsical boy-picture.

"After a male baby has grown out of long clothes and triangles and has acquired pants, freckles and so much dirt that relatives do not dare kiss it between meals, it becomes a boy. . . .

"Boy is Nature's answer to that false belief that there is no such thing as perpetual motion.

"A boy can swim like a fish, run like a deer, climb like a squirrel, balk like a mule, bellow like a bull, eat like a pig, or act like a jackass, according to climatic conditions. . . .

"A boy is a piece of skin stretched over an appetite. A noise covered with smudges.

"He is called a tornado because he comes in at the most unexpected times, hits at the most unexpected places, and leaves everything a wreck behind him. . . .

"He is a growing animal of superlative promise, to be fed, watered, and kept warm . . . a joy forever, a periodic nuisance, the problem of our times and the hope of a nation. . . .

"Every boy born is evidence that God is not yet discouraged

with man. . . .

"Were it not for boys, newspapers would be undelivered and unread, and a thousand picture shows would go bankrupt.

"Boys are useful in running errands: A boy can easily do the family errands with the aid of five or six adults. The zest with which a boy does an errand is equalled only by the speed of a turtle on a July day.

"The boy is a natural spectator:

"He watches parades, fires, fights, ball games, automobiles, boats, and airplanes with equal fervor but—he will not watch a clock.

"The man who invents a clock that will stand on its head and sing a song when it strikes will win the undying gratitude of millions of families whose boys are forever coming to dinner about supper time. . . .

"Boys faithfully imitate their dads in spite of all efforts to teach them good manners. . . .

"A boy, if not washed too often, and if kept in a cool, quiet place after each accident, will survive broken bones, hornets, swimming holes, fights, and nine helpings of pie."

JOHNNY AND GOOD OLD ROVER

When Johnny was around two years old, his parents realized to their horror, that Johnny was afraid of dogs. He not only shied away from dogs he saw on the street, but he screamed in terror every Sunday when they went over to Grandfather's, and Johnny saw good old Rover.

Rover, who was so elderly he spent most of his time snoozing. Rover, the acme of amiability.

Things got to such a pass that Grandfather shooed good old Rover down in the basement prior to Johnny's arrival, just so there wouldn't be a scene.

Now, this attitude of Johnny's, thought his parents, just was not right. It wasn't normal. Everyone knows a boy and a dog are part and partner of a combination that has come larruping down the generations.

Father and Mother put their heads together to see if they couldn't evolve some system of getting wee Johnny friendly with dogs; and Eureka! an idea!

Why not get Johnny a puppy? Johnny wouldn't recognize a frolicsome ball of funny fur as a dog. So:

They got Johnny a puppy and—Johnny was delighted. He and that pup took to each other like Damon and Pythias.

And the weeks went past, until finally, Father figured it was time to take the next step.

He interrupted a wrestling romp that Johnny and Puppy were having, to say:

"Johnny, do you know that Puppy is just a little dog?"

Johnny gently kicked Puppy in the ribs and Puppy mouthed at his foot. Johnny wasn't much impressed.

"So," Father progressed, "you wouldn't be afraid of a dog, now, would you? You wouldn't be afraid of Rover, would you?"

"He's a big dog," Johnny objected.

"But once he was just a little puppy, like Puppy," Father patiently pointed out, and Johnny took that under consideration. Finally he asked:

"When can I see Rover? I wouldn't be afraid of Rover."

The next Sunday, Johnny preceded Father and Mother into Grandfather's house.

"Where's Rover?" he immediately asked and Grandfather, who did not know about this change of heart answered, "Why, he's down in the basement."

"I want to see Rover," said Johnny, and, while Father and Mother winked at a somewhat sag-jawed Grandfather, Johnny hied himself to the kitchen, and to the basement door.

Grandfather opened it. Johnny eased down the stairs toward the spot where good old Rover was sleeping the serene and rabbit-catching dreams of a venerable age.

Father, Mother, and Grandfather sort of hung down the basement stairs to see what would happen.

Johnny marched a straight line to Rover. "Hello, Rover," he said, and as Rover opened an eye, Johnny leaned down and patted Rover's head.

Thump! Thump! Thump! went Rover's friendly tail. He opened both eyes amiably, and Johnny crowed with delight. Just to show his complete confidence, Johnny kicked Rover and good old Rover bit him. . . .

TAIL OF A NAUGHTY MONKEY

Pulitzer Pete was chatting about the intelligence of pets with an ex-Navy chum of his, Joe, and Joe immediately began recounting the qualities of Beezer, a monkey who was long of tail and short of ethics.

"Beezer," said Joe, "was our mascot on a destroyer in the South Pacific. He was smarter than English mustard. But he was the doggonedest thief. He'd steal anything, and, if anyone took after him, you know what the smart monkey'd do?

"He'd run up on the bridge and sit down right beside the skipper!

"Yes sir," Joe grinned, "that Beezer was smart, but he got caught up with, and after that he was a model monkey if there ever was one. You see:

"Beezer carried on a feud with the cook, a Filipino. And it got so bad the Filipino tried to get himself transferred three times, and that had us all sore at Beezer, because that Filipino could really turn out good chow.

"The chief cause of the trouble between the cook and Beezer was eggs. Beezer loved to suck eggs, and he'd steal an egg every time he had a chance. And he had a way of eating the egg that made that Filipino do a war dance all over the deck.

"Beezer would grab an egg and run up the mast, and out on a yard-arm, and hang by his tail, and suck the egg, and then he'd throw the shell down at the cook, who'd be jumping around down below, waving a cleaver. Well:

"One day, the cook got his hands on Beezer, at least on that long tail of his.

"Beezer had sneaked in the galley and nabbed an egg, and the cook grabbed his tail, but—

"The cook had just been cutting up some bacon and had a lot of grease on his hands, and that monkey pulled his tail through those greased hands like, well, like greased lightning.

"So Beezer went up the mast, with the cook down below waving his cleaver and fouling up the air with a lot of very bad Filipino language. And, as usual, Beezer went out on the yard-arm, and wrapped his tail around it a couple of times, and started to hang from it, but—

"The grease he'd gotten off the cook's hands made the tail so slippery it wouldn't hold, and Beezer dropped 40 feet on his puss.

"It didn't hurt him any, but it sure surprised him. And the egg he was still holding smashed and went all over his face, and just then the Filipino caught up to him and made one of the sweetest place-kicks with him you ever saw.

"He booted Beezer high in the air, and he went sailing down an open hatch, out of sight and, out of mischief, because he never bothered that cook again."

WHY PUSSY! HOW COULD YOU?

Florence Taylor had her housework brightened the other day by the meter-reader, who apparently had a little extra time and seemed willing to turn the time into words.

"I sort of can't get over what happened to me yesterday," said the meter-reader. "It was while I was calling on a woman I call the Grouchess because that's what she is.

"She never has a cheerful word. She's always sour on the world. And she's always looking for trouble. Well:

"I went in there yesterday morning and said 'Good morning' and she said 'What's good about it?' and so I knew she was down to normal, so I started for the meter in the basement. The stairs are steep and very dark, and I'd gotten well down and for gosh sakes, she had two lemon meringue pies set on those stairs, and I scuffed against the meringue on one of 'em.

"And when I got down to the basement I kept thinking about what she was going to do when she saw that meringue was marred. It would be just like her to make me a lot of trouble. She might even call up the company and register a complaint. So I began to think about how I could get out of the jam I was in.

"The first thing I did was to wipe that meringue very carefully off my foot. And then:

"Over in the corner of the basement I saw the family tomcat. He was curled up and sound asleep. I walked over and picked him up and tiptoed him up the stairs to those pies, and shoved his nose in the meringue. Then I took him back down to the basement and dumped him in the corner. And he became very busy washing that meringue off his face and whiskers.

"Then I walked back upstairs where the Grouchess was waiting and I said:

" 'Lady, those are two beautiful pies you have on the stairs. It's too bad your cat got into one of them,' and she said: 'He did?' and I said 'Yes'm,' and walked out the door.

"When I was about half way to the house next door I heard the Grouchess' door open, and I looked back and out sailed that cat with her foot behind him."

JUST A SMALL BOY ON A BUS

The suburban bus was crowded (we learn from Clyde Marsh) when a father and his son—a boy about three years old—clambered aboard.

They found standing place in the aisle, the boy beside a big blond woman, her lap piled high with packages from the day of downtown shopping. The little chap was in spic-and-span visiting clothes. It was clear that he had been prepared for this trip with great care and affection. But he found it pretty tough going on that bus, clinging to his father's hand, and swaying to the uncertain movements as the bus went bumbling along.

Abruptly, the big, blond woman swung around to the man sitting next the window next to her and to his utter astonishment, piled all her packages on his knees.

Then, she lifted that small lad to her own capacious lap.

He turned out to be a shy little chap, and his only replies to her queries were shakes or nods of his head. He sat there, gravely content.

Finally, the father touched his shoulder. He said:

"Here's where we get off Son," and, to the big blond woman: "Thank you very much indeed, mam."

The boy slid down and followed his dad to the door. Then he stopped. He had recalled something. A social obligation. He turned to face that big blond woman and waved her a thankyou farewell, his teeth shining doubly white against his ebony skin.

SHE SHOULD

One of the city's traffic officers became highly enraged at an elderly woman who, after he'd flagged her to stay on the sidewalk, overlooked his motions and strolled calmly out into the street.

"Lady," roared the officer, "don't you know what it means when I hold up my hand?"

"I ought to," she snapped. "For the last 25 years I've been a school teacher!"

WITH A HOLE IN HIS PANTS

That Sunday morning, Elbert Ducknoodle did not doll himself up the way he usually does. He had basement business to attend to.

He donned an ancient shirt and a pair of pants with practically no seat in them, and he did not shave. The result is that he looked a great deal like Sixth Street and Michigan Avenue.

Around 10:30, the phone rang. His wife told him it was his

unmarried sister in Birmingham "and she sounds awfully excited."

"Look," wailed Sister, "you know I'm flying to Mexico, but the ceiling is zero, and the airline is sending me to Chicago on the Mercury, and I am hardly packed, and I have such a little time to get to the station and what am I going to do with my car when I get there?"

"Hold everything," soothed Ducknoodle. "Get in your car and drive to Southfield and Outer Drive and I'll pick you up in my car and get you to the station."

Since Ducknoodle merely was to drive Sister to the train, and since he had precious little time, he set forth as he was, with the breeze blowing through the seat of his pants.

Sure enough, he met up with Sister but—with Sunday traffic what it is, and the distance to the MC Station, they just about had time to make it. In fact:

The clearance was so close that Ducknoodle slammed the brakes on his car spang in front of the station, leaped out, leaving the motor running, grabbed Sister's suitcases, and pursued her.

Wildly, Ducknoodle looked around for a Red Cap, but no Red Cap was to be seen. Which is why Ducknoodle bulled his way past the gateman—and the two of them galloped through the concourse and up the steps and Sister, panting, fell aboard the train.

Ducknoodle leaped into the vestibule to set down the bags.

Came a gentle zooshing sort of sound, and the doors closed and Ducknoodle was under way, with his unshorn whiskers waving and the seat of his pants as seatless as they'd been in his basement. . . .

Ducknoodle frantically sought the conductor, who did not seem delighted to have such a mouldy character aboard the Mercury. Ducknoodle demanded the train be stopped. "I can't ride around in ragged pants," said he.

The conductor said the Mercury stops for no man; not even for a pair of pants with the seat out. The next stop would be Ann Arbor and how about paying his fare?

Ducknoodle shoved his hand in his pocket. He found he had a little less than two dollars. Then things went red. He said he didn't want to be on that dingbusted train and he would be bifurcated if he would pay.

Ducknoodle did not pay his fare, but he suspects his sister may have. Anyway:

Ducknoodle descended at Ann Arbor and after what seemed an endless wait, he started back to Detroit and to whatever had happened to his running car at the door of the station.

Ducknoodle was so distraught he turned to his seat-mate, a distinguished elderly gentleman, and recited his woes. The gentleman listened in frigid silence. When Ducknoodle was through, the gentleman's cold eye raked Ducknoodle's attire. He said:

"My advice to you, my good man, is that if you are going to tell your wife about this, you had better think up a better story than that." Then he buried his nose in a newspaper.

Ducknoodle hurried through folks who looked at him askance to the entrance of the MC Station.

His car was not there. He asked a police officer. The officer hadn't seen it. He called police headquarters. They didn't know anything about it.

He thought it must have been stolen but such was his state that he spent an hour and a half looking around through adjacent streets and—he found it! There it was, neatly parked. There was only one trouble—someone had the keys.

By then it was 10 p.m. and Ducknoodle bethought him of his wife. He spent a nickle of his remaining seven cents calling her. She screamed:

"Where have you been? I have the police looking for you."

"Don't you worry where I've been," blared Ducknoodle, "you get the extra set of car keys and get a taxi and come down here and bring me a pair of pants with a seat in 'em!"

Eventually, she arrived. Ducknoodle drove home. He was so mad at everything he refused to give Mrs. Ducknoodle any satisfaction beyond seething: "Don't you ask me any questions. I'll tell you tomorrow."

And on the morrow, he did, and things are pretty nearly back to normal, except for one small point: Somewhere in Detroit is a Good (and car-parking) Samaritan, who still has the keys to Ducknoodle's car. . . .

DRUG STORE CONVERSATION

Ep the Epicure walked out of the drugstore and into an argument of which he, briefly, was the auditor. The protagonists were:

A boy, presumably 15, with enough hair for three, a black and red shirt dangling to his thighs; a pair of baggy cotton pants, ending to the north of sweat socks that seemed to wrinkle at the thought of disappearing into a pair of saddle shoes that once were brown and white.

He was waggling an angry finger in the face of another 15-year-old whose hair lagged down to the ears, dusting the top of a black and red shirt dangling to the thighs, covering the top of a pair of dungarees rolled up to the knees, disclosing an expanse of goose-pimpled flesh before the start of a pair of sloppy white socks that disappeared into saddle shoes that once were brown and white.

"And you," said Cotton Pants, "just what are you anyway? You aren't a man and you aren't a woman."

"I am too a woman," snapped Dungarees.

"You don't look like a woman," snorted Cotton Pants. "You are a Sour Apple."

"I am not a Sour Apple," blazed Dungarees. "I am just being stylish."

"All I gotta say," stated Cotton Pants, "is no wonder the Rooskis think we are nuts if they see sights like you. By gosh," he added, "I guess we ARE nuts."

A DOZEN BOYS HAVE THEIR SAY

We leaned back in our creaking swivel-chair and studied the note several times. Then we stared at the ceiling and out the window at the clock on the Union Depot, which agreed with our wristwatch and the clock here in the Youth Center, and then:

We sighed, for a reason some father or other of boys once small, now well-grown, may understand:

W. W. Ottaway, of the Port Huron *Times-Herald,* teaches a Sunday School class of a dozen 12-year-old boys.

Last Sunday he asked that each boy write the name of the man he most admired. The score:

President Truman	1
Pitcher Newhouser	1
Halfback Blanchard	1
Senator Vandenberg	3
My Dad	6

A SIX-BUCK LIMIT

Ann was loitering in a smallish florist shop when in came a mid-aged woman, quietly dressed and with an obscure face.

"I'd like," she said, shyly, "to buy something for a funeral. Let's see," and she began counting fingers, "there's Grace and Helen and Edna and Josie and Hattie and myself, that's six—what can we get for around six dollars?"

"I could fix you up with some gladioli and carnations and mums," said the florist.

"Mmmm," the woman mmed, and glanced into the big plate-glassed refrigerator.

"How about those roses?" she asked softly.

"No," from the florist, "I couldn't let you have those for six. I could fix them up for you if you'll go as high as $10."

"The hell we will," the woman blazed. "That man worked us overtime and never paid us a cent. Six bucks is plenty."

PRECISELY SO?

This item is dedicated to those perspiring parents who, of an evening, loyally come to the aid of their offspring when said offspring are doing their lessons:

Mrs. S. Borgula was paying less than her normal amount of attention to her three-year-old daughter, Jo-Jo.

In fact, Mrs. Borgula was so silent her husband began wondering if anything was the matter with her. So he turned to Jo-Jo, the fount of all information, with:

"Jo-Jo, where's your mother?"

Jo-Jo had her answer, prompt, pithy, and to the point:

"She's with Lorraine." (Her 10-year-old sister.)

"And what," demanded Borgula, "is Lorraine doing?"

"Oh," said Jo-Jo, negligently, "she's helping Mother with her homework."

SHE WENT MODERN

Herschell Hart, of WWJ, is telling of an ultra-modern Miss Four-Years-Old and her ultra-modern reaction to a Christmas present her mother bought for a little girl who lives in the neighborhood.

This was a tiny cradle with a baby in it, and sitting beside the cradle, the figure of a woman in flowing robes.

"Oh, I know what that is," exclaimed Miss Four. "That is the cradle with the Christmas child in it."

"And," encouraged her proud mother, "who is the lady?"

"Oh," said Miss Four, of 1946, "some sitter, I suppose."

WRONG PEW?

When the Rev. Al heard that the daughter of one of his parishioners had been pretty badly injured in an automobile accident, he larruped over to the hospital to call on her.

After he'd finished with that call, he decided he'd better drop in on the young woman who had been with her, and who also had been hurt.

The Rev. Al had gathered this second casualty was in the next room, so he barged in there, on reverential tiptoes.

The young woman looked at him. The Rev. Al went into action:

"I know you don't know me," said he, "but I'm the Reverend Albert Perry, and I just wanted to drop in and tell you how sorry I am about your accident."

The young woman answered:

"Mister, there's some mistake around here somewhere. I am in here because I had a baby yesterday and, believe me, it was no accident."

BRIGHT BOY

Bill met a friend of his, Carl, a pre-med student at a state university. And Bill couldn't miss the big grin Carl was wearing around his neck.

"What's happened to you?" Bill demanded. "Did you get an 'A' on a tough examination?"

"Oh, better than that," Carl crowed. "My morale got a real boost today—

"I took one of those psychology maze tests, and what do you think? They said I'm as smart as 92 per cent of all white rats, and 86 per cent of all feebleminded children."

PETE'S PAL AIN'T SPEAKIN'

Pulitzer Pete was staring out the window when he suddenly began to snigger:

"You see that big guy that just went past?" he demanded. "He used to be a friend of mine, and then he wasn't and all on account of my being helpful.

"That guy," Pete went on, "is a policeman and very sentimental and a few days before Christmas a few years ago he was talking about what Santa was going to bring his three kiddies, so I said:

" 'Why don't you go rent yourself a Santa suit, and come in and give those kids a thrill?'

"He thought that over and he figured it was a swell idea so

he did rent a Santa suit and he and his Missus made a lot of plans:

"He was on the afternoon shift so he couldn't come jinglin' in on Christmas Eve, so his Missus told the kids:

" 'Santa probably will get here Christmas morning—maybe just when you are eating breakfast.'

"So there were the kids trying to eat their porridge when there was a knock on the back door and the Missus said:

" 'Probably that's Santa now,' and she opened the door, and there was my friend in his bright red suit and patent leather boots, and a bushy white beard 'way up to his eyes.

"And the kids sort of moaned 'It's Santa!' and just then the family Airedale came roaring out of a corner and bit the bottom right out of Santa's britches. . . ."

ELSIE MADE HER POINT

Quite a thrill of excitement went through Aunt Mary's mind when she discovered that Elsie, her four-year-old niece, never had heard "A Visit from St. Nicholas," or "The Night Before Christmas," Clement Clark Moore's undying verse.

Here was a chance, thought Aunt Mary, to see exactly how a small child reacted to a first reading. So she started, with little Elsie listening as carefully as a congressman heeds his constituents.

When Aunt Mary finished, she asked: "Well, Elsie, what do you think of it?"

"Read the part again where the little girl was sick to her stummick" was Elsie's somewhat unexpected reply.

Aunt Mary goggled and said: "Why, there's nothing in that poem about a little girl being sick to her stomach," but—

"Oh yes there is," Elsie insisted, so Aunt Mary went back and began reading again.

She went through the first few lines, casting a questioning eye at the attentive Elsie, and nothing happened. Then she declaimed:

"I sprang from my bed to see what was the matter.

"Away to the window I flew like a flash,

"Tore open the shutter and threw up the sash—"
"See!" crowed Elsie, "she WAS sick."

IN ANN ARBOR

In an English class test in Ann Arbor not so long ago, the professor, properly a purist, addressed his collection of lads and lassies, sternly:

"This is merely a routine test, but I want to warn you that I will give a flat 'E' to any student in this class that uses in the test two of my pet aversions. One of them is 'swell' and the other is 'lousy'."

The class listened in silence. The professor demanded: "Now, before you start this test, are there any questions?"

And a cooing co-ed immediately came in with: "Just one, Professor. You haven't told us yet what the words are that are your pet aversions!"

THIS IS AMERICAN:

For two days prior to that important Senior dance in one of the city's high schools, this young miss of the Senior Class was the spark-plug of the group that did the decorations.

Most of the clever designs were her ideas, and they were brought into being by her presence and handiwork.

She worked with a will, and with a smile, never showing the way she felt that she was not going to be at the dance, because she did not have a date. . . .

EACH ACCORDING TO HIS LIGHTS

If you've really been getting up early during the Christmas season, and if the sky was clear, you may have noticed that the planet Venus has been a bright blaze of beauty, low on the horizon. . . .

The other predawn the phone rang on the desk of the Dog-Watch Editor, and a man's excited voice, heavily freighted with a Yiddish accent, said:

"Mister, have you seen that bright star in the sky?"

The Dog-Watch Editor answered: "Yes, it's Venus."

"I've never seen such a star," the voice asserted. "Not in all my life. You should take a picture of it and put it in the paper, it is so bright."

The Editor said: "That star appears around this time of year every year. . . . It is brilliant, isn't it?"

"Brilliant," the voice gasped, "that star is so bright I can count every one of its six points."

COULD SHE AVOID THAT TEMPTATION?

The talk at the After-Breakfast-Coffee-Club was all about slippery driving and devious ways of keeping skiddy cars under control.

It was generally agreed that a lot of super-scientists should stop fooling around with improved atom bombs and start devising sane methods to help winter-driving. And then:

"Which somehow reminds me," observed The Cartoonist, "of a friend of mine, in just such weather, who got one of those streaks of talking about the Future.

"He and his wife were sitting in their living room, staring into a bright fireplace, and his wife had just finished telling about having been stuck with spinning wheels twice that day on glare ice. Then silence came, and Hubbie abruptly changed the subject with:

" 'Dear, when I die, I would like to have my remains cremated, and the ashes put in an urn on the mantlepiece.'

"His wife answered, dreamily: 'They would be an awful temptation on a slippery day.' "

'TWAS EVER THUS

Alcib says that Letitia, who loves to listen to grand opera, became greatly agog when she learned that over the air was to come Traviata, one of Letitia's favorites.

She did not even frown when she found that Traviata would come in two sections, a week apart, because, after all, real music on the radio is worth the waiting for.

The day the first half of the double-header came through found Letitia settled in a comfy chair, with the static banned, and her mind ready for the musical treat—perhaps the better prepared because outside, the heavy snow kept falling. . . .

Traviata began to unfurl and almost immediately the doorbell began to ring.

Letitia stamped to the door. It was her neighbor, with her car stuck in a snowdrift, and a pressing appointment with the hairdresser. Letitia did her good turn. She managed to get that car unstuck just as the last of the first afternoon of Traviata was finished. However:

Letitia consoled herself with the fact that she liked the second half better, anyway, and, through the week, she kept looking forward to it.

Came the hour, the minute, the moment for it to start, and it did start, just as the front door bell started ringing.

In breezed Letitia's sister and her brother-in-law.

Sister settled right down and began talking about trivialities through the strains of Traviata. After a few moments, Brother-in-Law sauntered over to the radio and twisted it to another station. . . .

THEY DID NOT STAY 'SNOWED IN'

Just about the time the news of the death of Tommy Reed began flitting by rural telephone from North Hatley, P. Q., Can., to remote farmhouses over the Minton Hills, and out Suffield way, the Big Snow began to fall—

One of those silent snows, riding no wind; with smallish flakes that keep coming down, until the snow already on the frozen ground is buried one foot, two feet, three feet deep—

A barrier of white that crunches under foot, and squeaks complainingly in the zero cold, and makes the automobile as useless as a kiddie-car.

And so, Tommy's family, in Hatley, did not expect much of a "turnout" at his funeral.

How could there be, when the whole countryside had been snowed in? . . .

Of course, in the village itself, the snowplow dug out the main streets, and the road to the cemetery, and it made a special turn up the steep, sharp knoll to the Universalist Church, where Tommy had been going for more than 70 years. And—

The plow went one push beyond, scooping the heavy blanket from in front of the carriage sheds—

Carriage sheds! Relics of another day, standing there almost forgotten behind the church.

Sheds, that, before the benzine buggy commandeered the country roads, at church time, of a Sunday, found the farmers' horses stamping and switching at the pesky flies, in summer; or hunched under their blankets, in winter, with their breath gray-white on their shaggy chests. . . .

And it is just as well the snowplow did take that added twist, because at funeral time—

They began to show up, those farmers from the far, high hills and sheltered valleys folded in between.

Riding in sleighs, they came, with bells brightly a-jingle in an air so cold it plumed the snorts of horses bending to their task.

And we suppose the fact that they arrived at all, is all that really matters in the mention of a funeral so far away, unless, within this item is the measure of the man he was: friend T. V. Reed, who died on the day of the Big Snow. . . .

How easy it is to send a wreath of flowers at the time of the death of a city friend; or take a taxi to the funeral home.

How different, there in the Green Mountain country, where those friends, their side-roads filled in places four feet deep, shoveled their way through level snow and giant drifts besides, that they might travel four or five miles, even 10, to pay their last respects to Tommy Reed. . . .

CONTENTMENT

They have been married more than 10 years—years of close companionship; the closer perhaps, because there have been no children.

They held hands in the movie the other night, during a show in which the travel-hungry hero listed the "three most wonderful sounds in the world." He said they were: The rattle of anchor chains; the whistle of a train; the roar of an airplane motor.

As they came out of the movie, he said to her, casually:

"What would you say are the three most wonderful sounds you've ever heard?"

She answered softly: "Mendelssohn's Wedding March, as they played it when we were married; and 'Vienna, City of My Dreams,' while we were on our honeymoon. And the third? Well, when you are late to dinner, and the phone rings, and it's your voice."

WELL TRAINED . . .

Ernie the Woost thinks that Pianist Vladimir Horowitz would be interested in knowing how his dazzling technic impressed two gents in the audience:

They started out with an amiable argument about who should pay for the seats. Then, their comments turned to the world of music and it became clear that neither was too long on longhaired music.

But they could be impressed.

As Horowitz left the stage at the "mid-evening pause," one said:

"Gees, Joe! How c'n a guy make his hands go like that on a piano? I bet he musta done that a thousand times to go so fast. I guess it's all a matter of training."

"Sure it's a matter of training," Joe agreed, sagely. "And speaking of training:

"You shoulda seen the seal I saw up at the Sportsman's show. He could not only clap his flippers in front of him, but behind his back. Think of the training he had to have to do that! . . . Him and Horowitz!"

WILL THIS METHOD EVER BE POPULAR?

Mrs. Salvo took her six-year-old son to his first church wedding the other evening.

As you would expect, he was all eyes and ears.

Before the ceremony started, he studied the decorations, and seemed to be particularly impressed by the beauty of the altar, glowing in the gentle light of numerous candelabra of lighted candles.

At least, that is the impression Mrs. Salvo had until young Mister Six turned to her and stage-whispered:

"Hey, Moms, do those candles mean that's how old the bride is?"

STRAW THAT BROKE THE BUYER'S BACK

The suburbanite we'll call John Q. Blink at last received the long-awaited phone call.

His name had come up to the top of the car list. His new automobile was ready. "Come and get it," cooed the Dealer.

Joyfully, Blink hied himself to the salesroom, and gazed in rapture at the shining new car. Then Blink asked for the bill.

Blink blinked at the total but there it was—all neatly tabulated:

This for a radio; that for a heater; for a spotlight; for fog lights; for fender-guide lights; for exhaust extension; for fender-flaps; for a device to squirt water on his windshield; for a cigaret lighter.

Even flower vases had been installed inside and the charge carefully itemized.

Blink blinked, and then blinked again: At the very bottom of the list was an item: "License plate sign—$1."

"What's that?" he asked curiously. The salesman showed him:

Mounted over the rear license plate was a shiny tin sign bearing the dealer's name.

"You mean I got to pay for that, in addition to all the other junk I don't want?" Blink roared.

"That's the way our cars come equipped," the salesman coldly retorted. "If you don't want the car, as is, plenty of others do."

Silently, Blink wrote out a check for the full amount. Silently he marched toward that car. He grabbed that sign and, with a mighty heave, he wrenched it off. He bent it together. He hurled it to the floor. He jumped up and down on it. As he jumped, he hissed:

"Maybe you can make me pay for it, but you can't make me do your advertising for you!"

WELL LOCATED

E. J. Bemis, of Bloomfield Hills, hied himself to Pontiac the other day, to confer on some matters mechanical.

He went into a crowded, smudgy machine shop, and began looking around for the office.

He couldn't seem to find one. But he did locate a large man in the middle of the place, scribbling with a pencil stub on a scratch pad.

Bemis went close to him and roared, above the din of the machines traveling at top speed:

"Where's the office?"

He of the scratch pad, tapped his forehead with the pencil stub and responded:

"Right here."

GOOD FOR GRANDMA

Garnet Bertrand, who's sixteen years old, had a new photograph taken for Christmas.

Among those who received it was, of course, Grandmother, who is inclined to be on the conservative side. Probably, in fact,

Garnet would say she's square as a bear—not even hep to the latest in flickers.

Beverly was looking at Garnet's picture in Grandma's presence and said:

"You know, Garnet looks quite a lot like Alan Ladd!"

Grandmother sniffed. She said: "He's a lot better looking than Alan Ladd is, whoever Alan Ladd is!"

BUTTONED TO A POST

Herewith the way in which Traffic Officer Walter Zenith Watson created a traffic jam at the Union Depot, where he tries to keep traffic untangled:

He buttoned a drunk to an electric light pole, and that was too much:

The drunk came wavering through taxis, trucks, and cars, obviously so much out of control he was going to fall down and get hit. Watson had to do something, but there's no call-box at that corner from which he could summon the well-known Black Maria.

Watson knew he'd have to go in the depot to call the wagon, but what was he going to do with the drunk in the meanwhile?

This is what he did: He supported Mr. Drunk to a light pole, opened Mr. Drunk's overcoat, pressed Mr. Drunk's stomach against the pole, and buttoned the overcoat on the far side of said pole.

This had Mr. Drunk standing up so straight he couldn't possibly get himself killed. Although he did mumble querulously to himself when Watson left him there (bewildered, baffled, and perpendicular), and went in the depot to phone.

When he returned, commotion was rampant. Horns were squawking; drivers were howling; brakes were screaming because: About a hundred bug-eyed citizens were so intently staring at that gent in the strange strait-jacket they were standing in the street and giving no heed to the lordly automobiles.

Watson shooed the spectators away, untangled the traffic and, presently, along came the wagon. Whereupon Watson unbuttoned his drunk, who promptly collapsed into the arms of the wagon-men, either because of his alcoholic content, or because of his complete confusion at having been a human scarecrow. . . .

O EVE!

It may be that considerable light was cast upon the famous Apple-in-Eden situation during Sunday School recently, when Miss Teacher told her class of small children that story in dramatic detail.

Miss Teacher did such a good job of describing Eve's activities that there was a deep silence at the end of her dissertation—

So deep a silence that Miss Teacher felt justified in asking: "Are there any questions?"

Whereupon a wee miss with a big bow atop her head, leaned forward and asked, confidentially, as one woman to another:

"Was the apple good?"

A CASE OF OH SLUSH

One of those snowy, slushy days, Mrs. Ruth Ford was standing at a curb in Ann Arbor, rather ruefully regarding the goodly lake that stretched ahead of her, if she wanted to cross the street.

Next to her stood two members of the genus ex-GI, readily identifiable by their service coats, a slight stubble of beard, and a general atmosphere of Having Been There.

One of these chaps was short and square; the other long and lean . . . Mrs. Ford probably would not have noticed them much had it not been that Shortie suddenly snorted: "F'r Pete's sakes, look there!"

"There was across the street, where stood a beautifully Chesterfielded model of campus slicker, his hair painfully parted, his coat flaring, and his black knit necktie bearing the proper Windsor knot.

With him was a young woman, a really good-looking campus queen, staring at the slush beyond the curb.

Abruptly, the young man swooped over. He picked up that

young woman and waded her across the street. He set her gently on the curb a couple of feet from the ex-GIs.

The young woman slid out of his arms and smiled bewitchingly at him.

He bowed back at her, and at that moment Shortie came to life. He swung to Longie, bowed elaborately and said, in a loud if cooing voice:

"Oh! DAR-ling, allow ME!" With which he picked that big lug up and lugged him, simpering, across the street.

SHE'D SHOW HIM!

To be blunt about it, that young man up and handed that young woman the mitten.

Then he went to Florida, leaving her seething.

Precisely where in Florida he is hibernating, she doesn't know. Which doubtless explains the remark she made yesterday to a girl-friend:

"I just wish I had his address to write to, so I wouldn't write to him."

MOTHER FOUND OUT!

Immediately after eight-year-old Billy became the proud owner of an autograph book, he asked his mother, Mrs. David, to put her signature in it. Then:

Off to school he went with the book, to gather in the names of his favorite teachers.

That afternoon he reported "I got their names, and I sort of put down a word before and one after 'em, sort of to describe 'em."

This was enough of a statement to have Mrs. David delving into that book, when Billy wasn't around. She found:

"Social Studies—Mrs. Mueller (Units).

"Library—Miss Coye (Books).

"Art—Mr. Walker (Scissors).

"Gym—Mr. Livitsky (Fun)."

Having studied this listing, we think Mrs. David is to be pardoned if she wondered whether Billy had added anything to the autograph she had contributed. She turned to the first page. This is what she found:

"Mother—Mrs. David (Aggervation)."

WHAT'S IN A NAME?

This one may be old, but we've never heard it before. And there seems to be enough truth in it to pass it along:

Jimmy, who is now six, and whose movie attendance has been limited mostly to Saturday matinees, where the usher is the main law-enforcing officer, went last evening with his mother and a neighbor to a local theater.

When he heard his mother whispering to her companion, he nudged her and hissed:

"Sssh! Maw. Not so loud. Here comes the Husher."

MIAULISH

Said one of the two women on the bus, to her woman seat-mate: "And she tells me that every time she gets down in the dumps, she buys herself a new hat." Said the other woman: "I've always wondered where she bought her hats."

TABLE ETIQUETTE

In a "test" kitchen here in town the other day, the cooking expert in charge was the smiling hostess to a batch of bobby-soxers.

After teaching them a few simple recipes that should, in the future, be short-cuts to a man's heart, the cooking expert chanced to mention the proper way of setting a table.

The bobby-soxers displayed a lively interest, and somehow or other this intricate matter led to the subject of table etiquette.

And what particular phase of good table manners do you think brought out the greatest number of queries? It was:

"When I get to the table, where do I park my gum?"

FURTHER PROOF?

If you remember the sentient story about Fred and May, whose new hat drove the thoughts of mere money from her mind, you may be interested in this report from Florence Collins:

"That story reminded me of an incident regarding a hat which has been coming back to my mind time and again since it happened last November:

"About 10 days before my husband's mother passed away, I received a call to come as soon as possible to her home in Ohio.

"Since I went by train, I naturally dressed for the trip as properly as I could, and in my ensemble I included by newest millinery creation.

"When I arrived at Mother's home, I found that she was in an apparent coma.

"She had not talked, except in a whisper, for several weeks.

"I went into her room, hardly expecting her to recognize me but—she did. She looked up at me with sunken, misty eyes.

"She seemed to be thinking of something and trying to express it. Finally, in clear, audible words—the last words she ever spoke aloud—she said:

" 'I like your new hat!' "

WHO'S REVENGED?

If you ever have harbored a desire to blast somebody completely, and if you have stumbled upon a phrase you feel would do the dynamiting, you may understand the attitude of Mrs. Charley:

Quite a while ago she thought of something to say to someone she resented that would be completely unanswerable, and this something she carried around like a chip on the shoulder of her mind.

And, of course, her chance came:

She, her husband, and their youngsters were about to slide into a downtown parking place, when a large policeman came out of nowhere and boomed:

"You can't park there. Move on!"

Since Husband Charley could see no signs saying he couldn't park there, he started an argument. So the officer's face grew more prognathous as he intoned the Law, ending up with another "Move on!"

Here, realized Mrs. Charley, was her golden chance. She rolled down the window on the passenger-seat side, stuck her head out, and yelled at that officer:

"Did you ever try Castoria?"

The officer's jaw sagged to his chest. His eyes grew glazed with staring, and Mrs. Charley was savoring the sweet fruits of victory, when abruptly the officer pulled himself together and very sweetly he responded:

"Yes, lady. And I tried Lydia Pinkham's, too, and even that didn't help my disposition—MOVE ON!"

SURE PROOF!

Mrs. Walter Carroll is frank to admit that she's learning more every day about the younger segment of the younger generation. For example:

Marilyn, her seven-year-old daughter, came home from school the other day and reported, with much excitement, that one of the girls in her class "has a boy-friend."

Mrs. Carroll inquired:

"How do you know that?"

Marilyn put on that expression of patience, the air of infinite patience a child must have to get along with a parent, and replied:

"Why, Mother! I know he's her boy-friend because he chased her all the way home from school and hit her over the head with his school bag!"

'SUGAR SNOW'

Sunday afternoon we stood in the living room looking out the window at the big snowflakes sifting restlessly around, as if they were not sure where they should alight.

"In North Hatley," we announced, to a Mrs. Mama and a Son Seventeen who were buried eyebrows deep in Sunday papers, "In North Hatley, P. Q., Can., we used to call this sort of snow 'sugar snow.' "

"Mmmm," said Mrs. Mama.

"Because," we went dreamily on, "this is the kind of snow that begins to fall when the first crude cawing of the crows says that spring is on the way—When the maple syrup is boiling in the big pans over the red fires in the sugar houses, and every tree wears a white apron, and—"

We paused. Our audience wasn't exactly attentive. But you let us get the bit in our teeth and that doesn't matter a bit.

"In fact," we stated stoutly, "I called Uncle Bob in North Hatley last night, while you two were losing the basketball game for Grosse Ile, and he said that in North Hatley the sap is beginning to run."

"What's his name?" inquired Mrs. Mama, vaguely.

SORT OF REFINED . . .

It lamentably is true that Eric the Badger got nosed over to the side of the highway by the Pennsylvania State Police during a recent trip he made there.

According to the way the State Trooper looked at things Eric was by way of being a bad boy. But that's not the point of this bitlet.

The Badger says he does not believe the Detroit traffic police have "the refined approach" that trooper showed. The trooper silkily inquired:

"Pardon me, Sir, but may I see your beginner's permit?"

REWARDED

It was Dick who had lunch the other day with a man who's well established in the music-publishing world now.

To see the flair to his ties and the elegant roll to his lapel you'd never know that he'd known, well enough, the gaunt features of poverty.

Somehow he got to talking about how he left home to be a musician—and much against his father's wishes. His father had wanted him to stay in the small town where he'd been born, and to continue his education, and become a minister.

However, his father finally yielded to this man's determination to follow his bent, and away the man—we'll call him Will—went, carrying with him his father's gift—a large Bible, and bearing carelessly his father's final word: "If you get in any sort of trouble, read your Bible." Well—

Will eventually did get into some trouble. Lack of food trouble. To such an extent that, swallowing his pride, he wrote his father for $20.

You can imagine how he felt when his father wired right back: "Read your Bible. Especially the Ninety-first Psalm."

Will muttered some words that weren't any too religious, and slumped in the chair in the room out of which he was going to be evicted the next morning. And behold, the Bible was on the lower part of the one table, covered with some music manuscripts that publishers hadn't appreciated.

Will grabbed the Bible and, as might be expected, after quite a lot of thumbing around, managed to find the Ninety-first Psalm. Out fell two brand new $20 bills.

KILLER'S SON

"Pretty Boy" Floyd (nearly forgotten now) was once known the breadth of this nation as a ruthless killer. Not the least of Floyd's crimes was the legacy he left his nine-year-old son. It is a legacy of shame that will grow with the years.

The boy doesn't realize it today. It may be months before it begins to come home to him—come home in the cruelties that will be practiced upon him for Youth is so intolerant, bitter, brutal. The little fellow who has a twisted foot, starts school without knowing he has a twisted foot, but the rest of the "kids" tell him soon enough. Point japing fingers at him; jeer with a cruelty that is almost incomprehensible. And this youngster, Jack Dempsey Floyd, will go on through his boyhood years, crippled as surely as though his foot were twisted, because his father was what he was.

"Pretty Boy" Floyd. Robber. Killer. Father of a nine-year-old boy! "Pretty Boy" Floyd, the man with a record so bad that a good many millions of persons who are not bloody-minded, breathed a sigh of satisfaction when the news flashed through that Floyd was dead. But—out in the Oklahoma country, when that bulletin leaped along the wires, to a little house in the folds of those elusive hills, in the early evening, when the bare cottonwood branches reached tortured fingers toward the impersonal stars, the news came to the Killer's Son, Jack Dempsey Floyd. And afterward he sat, dry-eyed, working a crossword puzzle, this boy whose killer father had been killed.

Yes, not the least of the crimes of "Pretty Boy" Floyd was the legacy he left his son! But—it will take an aching period before young Jack Floyd sees anything in his father except a hero—how can you expect a nine-year-old to see his father as the world sees him? Does your small son, for instance, see you as the world sees you?

People talk about the fidelity of dogs to their masters; they praise the way in which a dog will stand for beating, starvation, cruelties, and still will love his master. True as that may be, it is nothing, compared to the devotion of a small boy for his Dad. . . . That's the most beautiful devotion I know.

The little fellow lavishes his love in small and puppy-like gestures. He is always under his father's feet. He is always edging in on what his Dad is doing. He is frequently a little pest, but deep in his eyes is adoration. He condones coldness; he overlooks a lack of interest in the little events of his life which, to him, are so important; he brushes aside a careless inattention and still comes on, admiring, adoring, striving in every shy, and artless, and artful way he knows, to cling close to this great big man, this man who can do everything; this man who, kind or cold, attentive or abrupt, smiling or peevish, is his Dad.

Fathers there be by the million who recognize this devotion; who realize the wonder of it, and yet, in the rush and worry and strain of living, so many of these fathers cannot keep themselves in hand.

So many a father flares up when he doesn't want to flare up; snaps cross words when cross words are a slap in the face; or buries himself in a book when there's a little fellow there, just bursting to tell of the way in which in school, he actually added thirteen and twenty-one and got thirty-four!

And oddly enough, that same father, that impatient father, that night, when the boy is in bed, all washed and warm and sleeping, will look down at him and wonder why it is that he cannot be worthy of the adoration so freely given by that son. Yes, standing there in the darkness, peering down at that tousled head, that impatient father resolves to be a better dad, if for no other reason than because he knows how few and fleeting are the years before that boy will see him as a giant no more.

And yet—there is something to be said for that impatient father; something that stems from the silly myth that "Love is Blind."

Love is not blind! Love is all too sharp of vision. It sees as through a magnifying glass! And thus it magnifies into a great fault in a small son, something that the impatient father would not even notice, or take very much for granted, in the lad who lives across the street.

And we suspect that in far too many cases this magnifying of the minor faults is what makes a man an impatient father. Because that father wants HIS boy to be the best and finest; and so, with nagging, scolding, sharp words, and sterner commands, that impatient father demands—too much. He expects perfection in this minute machine although he, after all his years of bumping into the harsh angles of life, is free to grant his own imperfection! Yes, it is so easy to demand too much, when love and pride are the spurs. And so:

If I could talk to a youngster who's just been needlessly squelched by his father, I'd say:

"Be patient with the old gentleman Sonny. He doesn't seem to understand you very well. He doesn't even seem to care to understand you. But—remember this—that father, who's grumpy sometimes, and changeable, is partly that way because he is fretting about you and your future; about the money that will give you the mental tools to hew you out a great success; about the snares that might snap shut around your growing feet. Yes—be patient with the old gentleman, Sonny, I can tell you something else—he loves you more, probably, than he will ever know, unless you leave him for another world, which Heaven forbid!

"So, Sonny, keep right on loving him, and here's a secret just between the two of us (a man who's getting fairly old, and you who still are young)—Yes, a secret between the two of us: Be gentle with your old gentleman, Sonny, because while he's your dad, the finest man in all the world, he is also (as your mother could tell you) just a little boy himself.

"A grown-up little boy, it's true, but in his heart of hearts, he often feels surprised to find that folks look at him as a man—that YOU regard him as the greatest man that ever was. Yes, a grown-up little boy with long, bright dreams—about your future—

"Do you know, he hopes you'll be a pitcher, and a sprinter, and an All American half-back. (He doesn't tell you so, he just dreams.) He hopes you'll be straight, and square, everything that's fine. And Oh! How he hopes that, as you grow, you won't grow away from him!

"So, Sonny, be gentle with the old gentleman and mark this well—he may never say it, but in the silent places of his soul, he dreams about the man you're going to be—A better man, by far, than he. . . ."

HIS MARBLE-BEARER

If you chance to read into this report about Butch and his Marble-Bearer, an overtone of wistfulness, or envy, it's not really our fault:

Butch is a high school senior, with shoulders like a blacksmith or, more to the point, like an All High School fullback.

In a little more than a month, Butch will be through with high school. He finds it pretty boring, right now, you understand, because he's been there so long. But—

It won't be boring that night when, with pomp and circumstance, he walks across the platform, and a strange man who, for four long years, he's regarded as just the superintendent, smiles at him and hands him his diploma.

No, it won't be boring then; and hardy as Butch is, there'll be an unwanted, unbidden jiggle to his Adam's apple; and he'll vaguely feel he's lost something that will never, nevermore come back. Yes—

Butch is a big senior, and so, of course, he is far beyond the marble-playing stage.

That's kid stuff, you understand, something for the grade-schoolers—the little guys who look up at Butch, with his three football rings on the left sleeve of his sweater, as they might look up at a legend on two feet.

The little guys who are always in his way, admiring, grinning shyly and often making of themselves, in their puppy-like adoration, a pest. . . .

But—the marble-season is in full swing and, well, even if you're a Senior, you can't help noticing all those kids down on their knees playing marbles, can you?

There's no reason, is there, why you shouldn't, at noon time, sort of stroll around and give 'em the bird? Why—

You might even unbend and show those brats how marbles should be played but—gosh, you couldn't very well, if you're a Senior, reach in your pocket and come out with some marbles, could you? Marbles, a badge of babyhood!

So, why not have, just like a hunter in Africa has a gunbearer, why not have a Marble-Bearer? Like, say, Robbie, who's a keen little kid—just a tenderfoot Scout, but a good Joe, with a lip that stays buttoned?

So Butch has a Marble-Bearer, that self-same Robbie, and Robbie bulged in three places:

In his two biggest pants pockets and in his chest, because:

Robbie's pockets contain the 149 marbles that Butch amassed during his salad days; and Robbie's chest bursts with the pride of the confidence Butch has given him.

And this is the way a Marble-Bearer works:

Butch wanders around the school yard and there are those little shavers, knuckling down. Butch plants his generous feet and observes:

"Aw, you kids aren't so hot. Now, when I was your age, I was a very greasy marble player."

And the youngsters look up, and one of them says, out of the freshness that is embarrassment:

"Betcha can't shoot one, two, three, with us."

And Butch sports the Senior snort and answered:

"Look, I'd take every marble you got, if I had any to play with," and then he spots Robbie and says: "Hey, Small-time, you got any extra marbles?"

Robbie beams, and dives in his pockets. He comes out with a handful. "Go to it, Butch," says he, on terms of high equality. So:

Butch, with many a derisive grunt, gets down on his knees, and goes to work. Now:

Either he wins or he loses. And oddly enough, and yet, not so odd at all, those little fellows secretly hope he wins. If he loses, he says, rather grandly:

"Say, you kids're pretty hot," and then to a gloomy-visaged Robbie, hovering on the rim of the human circle. "Don't worry, Robbie, I'll pay you back." But—If he wins, and he nearly always does win, either because those little fellows let him, or are in awe of him, or because he actually was a slick shooter when he was just a little kid, all of four years ago—if he wins, he says:

"See, I told you! You boys got to go some to play marbles with me. I tell you what, though, I got no use for marbles, so you just pay Robbie back the ones he loaned me, and five for himself, and split the others up among you." And—

With that, he gets up and dusts his knees, and with a casual "S'long, splinters," he strolls sedately away from there, with never a thought to the glances that glow in round boy eyes, following his broad back and his All-High School shoulders as he saunters out of kidhood back into the supreme, the austere heights of Senior-Hood.

RIGHT SHADE

Edith Crumb has a friend who is the mother of three smallish boys who, as boys will, go galhumphing in and out of the house, bringing lots of mud and distress to a woman who likes to have her house looking well.

The other day this harried mother went into a home furnishings store, carrying a paper parcel under her arm and a determined expression on her face. She announced to the clerk:

"I want to buy a new living room rug."

"What color, madam?" he inquired.

The weary mother reached gingerly in the package she had, and brought out a boy's shoe. She said: "I want a living room rug to match the color of mud on this shoe."

UNDER THE BLANKET

A friend of ours who's heard the Philadelphia Orchestra a great many times, and was anticipating its appearance the next Wednesday evening at the Masonic Auditorium, got to wondering about a standard incident at each performance:

At the end of the program, as the applause wells up, Alexander Hilsberg, the concertmaster, arises and shakes hands with Eugene Ormandy, the conductor. And, under that blanket of applause, the two hold a very brief conversation. Well:

This friend got to wondering what those two said to each other, and, at a gathering not so long ago, she had a chance to ask Ormandy.

He looked slightly startled, and then confessed that the remarks between the two are highly impromptu. For example, on one occasion, Hilsberg, bowing from the waist, observed to Ormandy:

"A rabbit's foot to you," and Ormandy replied: "And a four-leaf clover to you, sir!"

When Hilsberg is otherwise uninspired, he's likely to say: "A Happy New Year," even if the evening happens to be in June. But the standard remark, especially on long concert tours, is for Hilsberg to point out:

"Well, one down and 24 (or whatever the number) to go."

HOME SWEET HOME

The mother of three children, whom she labels Seven, Two, and One, prefaces her report by the restrained remark:

"I dare any man to say he would have the patience to face the following incidents, all in one sweet spring afternoon:

"1. Baby One spills box of cereal on kitchen floor.

"2. Two opens refrigerator door and out pops an egg.

"3. Two swings a bat and breaks window in the front door.

"4. One tears a four-inch square out of living room curtain.

"5. Two spills bowl of veg. soup on her lap and dining room floor.

"6. One reaches from high chair and gets Seven's milk and spills it on high chair tray and dining room floor.

"7. Comes nap time, so Mother starts to prepare dinner. With burners covered with food, and her hand perhaps a little shaky from incidents 1, 2, 3, 4, 5, and 6, she drops tumbler on stove, scattering glass on food. Throws food out.

"8. Seven, coming home from school, drops bottle of pickles on basement floor.

"9. Husband, coming home from work, opens side (grade) door, pushing buggy and Baby One down stairs into basement. No great injuries aside from noise.

"10. Mother rushes upstairs to catch Two standing on arm of chair, getting down bottle of black ink.

"11. One drops bottle of peanut butter on bathroom floor.

"12. Husband, disgusted, puts on hat to go buy a drink. Stamps out of house, climbs in car. Backs car out and bumps into parked car. . . ."

LUNCH WITH WEECIL

Cecil the Weecil was feeling particularly puckish the day we had lunch with him.

We found that one of the tines of our fork had branched out for itself. Bluntly, it was a badly bent fork. Which is probably why the Weecil observed:

"That fork has seen better tines."

IN THE TWILIGHT

Many a man, and matron too, can be heard at the end of a day, these days, saying: "I'm traveling too fast. There is more in the day than I can possibly do."

Probably that's right, especially when the current strain, the often unspoken but frequently thought question comes up of where is America, our America, heading. But, on the other hand, there is tedium.

Tedium! The dull, drab drag of the uninteresting, the almost unwanted hours.

The other bright and benevolent afternoon, with spring whispering its promise through sunshine and unfolding leaves, we happened to be calling at an old man's home.

As we came out, around four o'clock, we glanced at the group sitting on the porch; sitting there with their canes and their memories, their faces, as Raymond Chandler once said, "like lost battles."

One of them made a remark to another. No words of ours could etch in print the utter world-weariness of that old man's voice—this ancient whose days go achingly on to their final rendezvous with eternity. He said:

"Only another hour and it'll be time to eat. And then, after that, pretty soon it'll be time to go to bed."

JUST A LITTLE CHINESE BOY . . .

Lieut. Robert S. Young, writing from Hongkong says: "I guess I have been most impressed so far by the little and cute (Chinese) kids who are, of course doomed—

"I would bet my life right now that half of them will not live to be 18. But they are everywhere, seething with activity.

"And some of them certainly get you. To cite an example:

"There is one little beggar—five or six years old—who has a tin sardine can, who walks around, saying:

" 'No mother, no father; no whisky and soda; just a poor little son-of-a-gun.' "

EXPEDIENCY

The one-row-at-a-time gardener who brought rolling eyes of anguish to diligent victory gardeners last season, has started up again.

He was out last evening, the one-row gardener, with his family in last year's formation behind him. But maybe we'd better explain about last year:

Quite early in the spring his wife announced at a gathering of neighbors, "We're going to have a garden this year," to which her husband snorted:

"Then you'll have to dig it yourself. No gardening for me."

Since this husband is known to be headstrong, the neighbors waited to see what would happen. And nothing did happen for several weeks—

Weeks during which the garden-addicts spaded up their plots, raked them, planted them, and began harrying away the eager weeds. And then, one early Saturday afternoon:

Forth from the home of the headstrong husband issued an odd procession:

First came husband, wearing a long-handled shovel over his shoulder and a grim expression.

At an awe-struck interval behind him trotted the eight-year-old son, carrying a small tin can.

Next was the six-year-old daughter, wrestling with a tin pail.

Last marched the wife-and-mother, bearing a rake over her shoulder and a veiled expression on her eyelids.

Reaching the edge of the plot where the garden had been planned, Husband squinted through the merrily growing weeds, and began to dig.

He turned over a spadeful of earth, and spatted it with a shovel.

Son squatted on the ground and picked up a couple of angle-worms.

Husband dug another spadeful. Son squatted. And thus—

The two of them progressed, in a reasonably straight line, from one side of the garden plot to the other. Having reached the far side, and with never a backward glance, Husband put the shovel over his shoulder and strode away, with Son trotting behind him.

Meanwhile Mother was following that turned-over soil and raking it into some semblance of pliability.

With the aid of Daughter, she produced a packet of seeds from the pail and planted them. . . .

Next afternoon, this procession again appeared, and exactly the same procedure proceeded.

Again, the sod-turning, in a straight line, approximately three feet from the digging done the day before. Again, but we said that before—the same things happened, including the planting of another packet of seeds.

And that same thing took place each Saturday and Sunday for the next six weeks:

Just those straight spaded rows, with the weeds waving in between and—oddly enough, the garden came along very nicely, in spite of them.

Perhaps as a reward to a wife who had hitched her wagon, if not to a star, at least to an ardent fisherman who'd conceded that since he had to dig angleworms, he might just as well dig 'em in a straight line.

ADMIRATION

We keep thinking of the implied compliment that lay behind the remark of small Forbes Mathieson the other evening:

One of the adults at a quiet gathering asked him, as adults almost invariably will:

"What would you like to be when you grow up?"

Forbes seemed a little hesitant, and his questioner elaborated with: "Do you want to be a policeman? a fireman? the Lone Ranger? or what?"

And Forbes answered: "When I grow up, Sir, I just want to be a father."

RESPONSIBILITY

Les pulled his car to the proper stop with the red light on Lafayette at Cass, in the forefront of the heavy west-bound five o'clock traffic.

Anne, in the front seat beside him, said: "For goodness' sake, look!" Both looked to the curb at the south side of the street.

A boy stood there, a boy perhaps five years old, his clothes rather ragged, and his face distinctly dirty. He was crouched over.

But it was not so much the boy that caught their attention as the fact that a smaller girl, maybe three, was crawling up on his back.

When she was settled there, the boy took a quick squint at the green light he faced and, staggering a little, he managed to lug that little girl, piggy-back, under all the tall noses of all those impatient cars.

He sat her tenderly down on the north curb, and the light on Lafayette went green.

Then happened a marvel of this automotive age—the west-bound cars did not spring into gear. Nor came a single impatient squawk from self-important driver. No—

It seemed as if every person in every car was staring at that tow-headed boy, with a girl so tow-headed she must have been his sister, standing safely on the sidewalk, with her tiny hand slid into his small fist.

Les eased into gear and for some time he and Anne drove in silence before they began to talk about that little "Street Seen," that bit out of a big city, that boy, too young by usual standards, to be out in downtown traffic dangers, caring for a child still younger.

They agreed, of course, that they will never know, but it may so be they had seen one of America's future great men, in this five-year-old child who already has learned the rugged, sometimes ruthless lesson of responsibility. . . .

CREAKING JOINTS?

If you chance to have lived enough of the automotive age so you sometimes, of a morning, find it pretty hard to get your feet under you, and even difficult to put your mind in gear, you might care to hear about a Mrs. Seventy-One who is still a sparkplug:

"I'm a little lame this morning," she confessed recently, and then she chuckled:

"Last evening I was listening to the radio, and the band—a very good one—was playing Strauss' 'Tales from the Vienna Woods.' So I jumped up the way I always do when the band plays a Strauss waltz, and I began waltzing around the living room. But—

"You know how fast the tempo of that waltz is? Well, I was keeping the tempo, and spinning around at a great rate and caught my toe in the rug and fell flat.

"I," she finished up, "bumped pretty hard, but, thank goodness,

I didn't break my glasses!"

POSSIBLY A FERTILE FIELD

Geraldine Mills is telling about the latest of the doing of Dennis Murphy, nine years old, who has Ideas.

Dennis and his dad were driving along, with Dennis deep in one of those fathomless silences into which the young can so unexpectedly plunge.

Abruptly he came to the surface to remark:

"Daddy, I know what I am going to be when I grow up."

"That's fine," said Father, his mind running over the usual ambitions of everything from policeman to pilot of a 1,500-mile-an-hour jet-plane.

"That's fine," he repeated; "what are you going to be when you grow-up?"

"I'm going to be a brain specialist," Dennis declared. "And, Daddy, you are going to be my first patient."

THEY KNEW HARRY

Mrs. Kenneth Groom was sitting sedately in a medium-filled street car when her attention was caught by a young man who suddenly sprang to his feet, saying: "I'll be doggoned!"

He charged up the aisle to where two other young men had just parked. He said: "Hi-ya, guys, hi-ya!"

Immediately the other two let out whoops of delight. And it swiftly developed the three of them were returned veterans who'd been in the same outfit overseas.

After a few moments of re-unioning, the young man who'd charged up the aisle, Tom by name, said: "Say! I saw Harry the other night."

"Harry?" a blank non-recognition in the tone of the other two.

"Sure," said Tom. "You know, Harry. Our first sergeant."

"Oh," said the other two, together, and made it sound like

swearing.

"Harry," Tom persisted, "is workin' in a roller-skatin' rink. Guess what his job is?"

Again came a joint answer: "Bouncer!"

"Correct," said Tom, and all three laughed and laughed and laughed.

HE COULDN'T

Fletcher R. Armstrong says he figures you can know who wears the pants (regardless of the figure) in the home of the hero of this incident, that happened right on Joseph Campau in Hamtramck:

The police department had installed a stern street sign reading: "No Parking Here."

Pretty soon, a beat-pounding policeman turned beet-red in anger because, right abreast that sign, which incidentally graced the side-walk in front of a super-market, a car was parked.

Over klumped the cop and at the smallish man behind the wheel, he blared:

"Wotsa idea? You wanna getta ticket? Move on, Stupe. Move on!"

To which the man behind the wheel answered with a firmness that seemed, somehow, entirely outside his own character:

"I can't move on. Not right now, officer. I'm waiting for my wife."

What's more, he wouldn't move and finally the officer lumbered away, muttering something about men and mice, or was it mice and men?

SKIPPER HAS IDEAS

Florence, accompanied by small son Skipper, was about to enter the Wyandotte Market when, with much blasting of horns, and ribbons rampant, a wedding party pulled up at the photographer's studio close by.

Out sprang the bride, the groom, and the gay wedding party. "What's going on?" demanded Skipper, who takes after his father.

"A wedding," Florence answered. "Those two have just been married" and, forestalling 1,001 questions, she added:

"They've been to church, and now they are going to have their pictures taken, and then there will be a big meal, and dancing, and everyone will have a grand time."

Skipper accepted this explanation without comment, as he and mother went inside the busy market.

Presumably, Skipper was thinking that his home-life could be enlivened by a good big meal and dancing and everyone having a grand time. Anyway:

He suddenly whooped, in a voice that echoed through the crowded market:

"Mother! Why don't you and daddy get married?"

WHAT SHE COULD . . .

We were chatting with the Lame Lady in a semi-hospital when, along the corridor, came the sound of a piano hit by strong fingers.

The notes merged into each other, and into an old, old, tune: "When You and I Were Young, Maggie."

We hoisted a quizzical eyebrow at the Lame Lady. She said:

"It's unusual for him to be playing in the afternoon."

We were silent, and it seemed as if we could hear a feminine voice singing those words—not the words of a song, any more, anyway, but nostalgia for a different, distant era.

The piano went silent. The Lame Lady went on:

"He comes to see his wife every evening. They are both in their early thirties. She is so completely paralyzed it takes two men to lift her into a wheel chair. Then he wheels her to that alcove where the piano is, and plays her favorite tunes."

The music welled up again: "Silver Threads Among the Gold."

We asked: "It almost seems as if I could hear a woman singing?"

"Yes," nodded the Lame Lady. "Her throat is just about all

that isn't paralyzed so—she sings."

A WINDOW IS A BOOBY-TRAP

Barc got aboard the bus, bumbled toward the rear and parked himself on the broad back seat next a soporific citizen reading a newspaper by the far window.

Barc seated himself, glanced around and found himself looking squarely into the eyes of an elderly woman with somewhat scraggly hair, holding down the end of the little seat acróss from him.

She smiled and Barc blinked. Then he sort of smiled back and began wondering where in the world he'd seen her before.

Half a block farther, she scrooched around and made an effort at opening the window behind her. Barc, the gallant, sprang to his feet with an "Allow me," and opened the window easily.

"Thank you," the woman murmured and opened her handbag, holding it up for his inspection.

Barc looked and frowned. All he saw inside were packets of shoelaces.

"Would you care to buy a package?" the woman asked softly.

Barc heard himself asking "How much?" and the woman answered: "Whatever you care to give."

Barc took one pair of laces, gave the woman a quarter, slumped back on the end seat and mopped his forehead.

At the next block a man got on, strolled to the rear of the bus and sat next to Barc. The elderly woman smiled at him. His eyes stuck out like tulip bulbs. He smiled back.

The woman turned and tried to get the window behind her, down. The man said "Allow me," and put the window down. The woman opened her handbag. The man goggled and, shortly after, stuffing a pair of shoelaces in his pocket he plopped down next to Barc, whistled to himself softly and went silent.

Two blocks farther, a man got on and ambled down the aisle to the back of the bus. He sat next to the man next to Barc. The elderly woman unfurled a smile at him.

The man r'ared back a bit. Then a watery smile he returned.

The woman turned around and ineffectually tried to open the window.

The man said: "Lemme do that for you, Lady!" He sprang to her aid and into her trap. He, too, with shoelaces, collapsed on the back seat, thereby filling it, with the other men, to a comfortable capacity. Well—

Barc studied the two men who'd been the woman's subsequent victims. He rather enjoyed the bemusement on their maps. Then he slued his left eye around toward the man who'd been aboard when he got on. This worthy was still reading his paper. Out of the corner of his mouth he said, loftily:

"Anyway, I got the only pair of white ones, Sucker."

Then, he went back to reading, and a silence of profound pensiveness blanked the four gents on the back seat. This endured until the bus reached the downtown end of the line. Barc got up to get off. So did the other men. So did everyone except—that elderly woman. She stayed put.

As Barc wobbled from the bus, he glanced back.

The woman was casually shoving down the window behind her.

DIFFERENT

The fifty-ish gent wasn't standing Friday's heat so well, and then someone up and asked him how he felt:

"I am old," he sighed, "and also antique."

"Aren't they the same?" asked his questioner.

"They certainly aren't," Mr. Fifty snorted. "If something is old, it's no use, but if it's antique, it's valuable."

HIS PLAN

Now that the Month of Brides has gone its way, we suppose there's no reason for holding back the observation of a father who has a daughter now nearing 16.

This father attended a whole drove of weddings during June, and was meticulous on each occasion to look over the presents to be darn sure the one he and his wife had sent was on display.

From which we suspect the month gave him a pang in the pocketbook, and as he heard from brides' fathers something about the cost of weddings, he grew more and more gloomy.

So, Sunday evening, he observed to his daughter:

"Now look, Connie, when you get around to being married, you don't need to be afraid to elope. In fact, I'll hold the ladder for you."

GRATITUDE

Directly after Gladys, a gushy co-ed at a nearby university, had learned, for sure, that she'd passed an English course through which she'd floundered, she made a point of seeking out the white-haired professor.

"Oh, professor," she gushed, "I just must thank you for the grade you gave me in your course. And I want to thank you for all the knowledge you taught me."

The professor answered, with polished ease:

"That's very nice of you, Miss Ducknoodle, but please don't bother to thank me for a trifle like that."

THE FLAG FLEW HIGH

Among the overseas letters that came to our desk during the war, one keeps recurring to our thought, whenever the Fourth of July comes around.

It was written in rather a shaky hand, in heavy pencil, on a couple of sheets of smudgy paper.

Its author was a Marine sergeant. It read (and reads):

"Dear Mr. Jackson: I'm writing this with the butt of a pencil on a tin can by the light of the setting sun, and I don't know why I'm writing it to you only I often think of you as a megaphone:

"You shout one person's thoughts to many:

"Maybe I've got that battle-fever, or battle-shock, or something. I know I sure am tired and maybe I'm a little out of my head. . . .

"I want to tell you, Mr. Jackson, no one has ever really seen the Stars and Stripes, until he has seen it raised over some territory that has just been taken from the enemy.

"The flag is up there right now, Mr. Jackson. It will come down pretty soon, but it will go up again in the morning.

"It is up there now, whipping, or standing straight out, and it sort of makes the sky more blue and the sun brighter, and the grass more green. No, Mr. Jackson, you never really have seen the Stars and Stripes, until you've seen our flag go up and up to the top of the staff, with maybe the guns still banging in the distance. . . .

"Up the staff, and catch a moment, and then spread out, bright and clean, up there, above the bodies on the ground below."

COURTESY

Dena Goldsmith is wondering if there is such a thing as thought transference between humans and dogs—seeing-eye dogs at any rate, as the result of the following happening:

Dena was on a street car and saw a seeing-eye dog. She looked at him and thought: "What a wonderful creature you are."

When the dog led his master past her a few blocks farther on, the dog kissed her hand. . . .

NO VACANCY

In a four-bed room at the Veterans' Administration have been lying, in amity, a Malaria, a Broken Neck, a Fractured Spine, and a Fractured Leg.

Malaria had a radio over which he, and the other three, listened to many a program.

One recent morning a nurse came in, brightly to say:

"Well, Malaria, you're going home in a few days, and we're

going to move you this morning to another room. The doctor's coming in to tell you."

The announcement brought but a grunt from Malaria and a complete silence from Broken Neck, Fractured Spine, and Fractured Leg—a silence so filled with something, though, that the nurse looked at them, and around the room:

"Say," she said, "that's a fine radio there. Whose is it?" and Malaria responded: "Mine."

"Is it the only radio in the room?" the nurse asked, and Fractured Leg said "Yes."

At that moment the doctor appeared. The nurse said:

"Doctor, I just found out that the bed we'd planned to take Malaria to is still occupied, so couldn't he stay here?"

Apparently it didn't make any difference to the doctor, because he nodded, negligently, but—it made a difference to Broken Neck, Fractured Spine, and Fractured Leg, because Broken Neck wrote us:

"So that afternoon we listened to a swell ball game and I guess there are some fine and thoughtful people in this world."

BLIND LEADING . . .

Ford Pettit was somewhat astounded when he saw a Doberman lead a blind man across Lafayette boulevard and smack into a utility pole.

ABOUT OLD MAJOR

There must have been a young Major once; and even a prancing, puppyish, slipper-hiding little Major but—

We can't imagine that. We can remember only serene and adult dignity, and a fine tolerance with childish whims.

Of course, Old Major was the fighting-est dog in town. What boy's first dog wasn't?

Of course, he was the wisest and the best. What boy's first dog wasn't? After all:

A boy's first dog holds in the mind of the man that boy becomes, something of the same position, inviolate and remote, in which a woman keeps enshrined her first sweetheart.

And as we thought of Old Major last evening, and guiltily realized it was the first time in months that he has marched across our mind, it seemed to us that Old Major was all good dogs in one. He was himself and yet he was, in part, our Mister Atkins. And Patrick, too, another splendid dog, who died. . . .

Yes, we felt, last evening, a slight sting of shame that it has been so long since we remembered Old Major. . . .

Old Major who padded shadowlike through our early childhood, his red tongue lolling, his banner of a tail a-slant like a bayonet.

We are sorry, now, we took him so much for granted but after all, that is the way of the young—they take so much for granted.

Children absorb, without surprise, the unexpressed but not always unrecognized sacrifices of their elders. They take such sacrifices as their due and after all, perhaps this is proper:

We oldsters live, in part at least, to repay to our youngsters the sacrifices our parents made for us.

But we wish we could more have appreciated Old Major in those days which now, so strange are the quirks of memory, that recollections of him are flitting pictures, half-caught and seen as the blue sky sometimes can be seen through shifting banks of August clouds.

We remember—we must have been around five—crawling under the front porch one summer afternoon.

Old Major was lying there—he must have been watching us through the trellis as we played.

He didn't thump his tail in welcome. He was too dignified for that. He was just there, if that makes sense. And we crawled close to his friendly silence.

A bee came buzzing along and we sat still as a stone.

The bee came close and—Old Major snapped at him. And we had a thought, warm as firelight in the winter's dusk: "He can't sting me. Old Major's here!"

He was Protection on four feet, Old Major was—the strain of mastiff crossed with St. Bernard. He had his own ideas about what should be done:

Our parents had to shut him in the barn when we went wading in the placid lake. Otherwise, before we'd reached an ankle-depth, Old Major had us, firmly and politely, by the brief seat of our pants, pulling us back to good dry earth.

So many pictures flitted through our mind, and then the latter one we still regret.

We'd come back to North Hatley, P. Q., Can., after a winter spent in Boston, Mass.

Back to friends and base ball and canoeing and swimming and the helter-skelter of boyhood excitement that makes each day complete unto itself; each day a shining pearl of happiness upon the pulsing throat of time.

It was late in the afternoon of home-coming day we strolled out in the back yard and there was Old Major, lying in the sun.

We had a quick twinge of shame that we hadn't looked for him the instant we returned. We hurried toward him. Toward that magnificent black coat, gone a little gray now; toward that sleek black head.

He lifted that head. His lips came away from his teeth and he growled—the throaty danger-growl we'd once heard when a stranger tried to speak to us. We froze an instant, while a world collapsed. And then we said, so softly: "Major!"

Just that one word and—that great head, dropped into the dust. The dust came up in dirty yellow bits. And that great banner of a tail, moved just a little, once.

We looked at those eyes that had followed us through so many years. And those eyes could not see us any more. Old Major, old Old Major, had gone blind. . . .

Ah well, we were far away again from Hatley when Old Major died—but, as we said, he walked again in memory last night. And that is why we write these words today. A tribute coming 40 years too late.

OVERHEARD

John Wilson couldn't very well miss the conversation between two young women standing at the counter. One said: "And she says she does the most filing of anyone in the department."

"Yes," sniffed the other, "of her fingernails."

CAN'T FOOL HIM

The cartoonist says there's a dentist in town who's back from one of those strenuous fishing expeditions.

He and a friend went to the Soo and then started traveling north under the confident wing of an Indian guide y-clept John Noseeum.

The fishermen and John got along very well indeed, so much so that abruptly John announced:

"Me takum to lake where fish jump in canoe. Nobody been there in six years. Gotta portage."

With this succinct statement, the two fishermen found themselves loaded down with camping gear, while John, himself, put a canoe on his head and started plunging through the brush.

Pretty soon John stopped at a tree and looked at it from under that canoe, something like a puppy peeking out from under a bureau. John grunted, and veered a little to the north. He stopped and took another peep at another tree.

About then the dentist spoke up with: "John, do you ever get lost?"

"Never get lost," asserted Mr. Noseeum emphatically. Then he added, after a hesitation: "Sometimes lake gets lost."

BACK TALK

We're not at all sure this incident should be put in print. It may be against the public interests. However:

Not so long ago after Mrs. John Waling moved from the congestion of the city to the wider-open spaces of Dearborn Township, she had a call from her nearest neighbor, a dumpy little elderly woman whose English bogs down under stress.

At the end of the call, the little lady invited Mrs. Waling, "Coom hover see me soomtim'."

As a result of that friendly bidding, Mrs. Waling is over at Mrs. Pzylcz's practically every day. Because Mrs. Pzylcz—but let's let action take the place of description:

No sooner than Mrs. Waling had been welcomed and Mrs. Pzylcz had produced some feathery cookies and a sturdy cup of stout coffee, Mrs. Pzylcz asked: "You like lissen radio?" and before Mrs. Waling could respond, Mrs. Pzylcz flicked on the switch.

Promptly an unctious masculine voice said, "Good afternoon, Ladies."

"Ooomp," sniffed Mrs. Pzylcz, "good afternoon yourself an' see how you like it," and turned to another station, whence came the start of another Washboard Drammer.

"Not eenterested," said Mrs. Pzylcz emphatically, and again turned the dial. This time a gent was praising the virtues of a certain type of sink. Mrs. Pzylcz exploded:

"Oh, hush your business. I got me a zink, a nice, vonderful zink. Vot I vant is better vater." And again she twisted the dial.

This time music came forth, hot and blue. Mrs. Pzylcz braced her fists on her hips, glared at the radio and demanded:

"For vhy ain't you play it the polka?"

With which she shut off the radio and chatted pleasantly with Mrs. Waling until she thought it time to go. Mrs. Pzylcz followed her to the door to observe:

"Coom back henny time you like. Next time mebbe you join me talkin' back mit dat dam radio."

SO TRUE

Madge was a trifle triumphant, but humble withal, when her wise-cracking husband Joe came home.

"The strangest thing happened at the Thursday Musicale today," she said.

"Yes," Joe encouraged.

"They had an election of officers," Madge went on, "and they put me on the board—and the strangest thing about it is that I am not at all qualified to be on the board."

"Oh, well," Joe yawned. "Every board has a splinter on it."

HOW TO TELL SOUTH

It all started when we grimly announced at lunch: "Someday, I am going to own a barometer."

Karl Lysinger snorted: "What do you want a barometer for? You couldn't tell what the weather is going to be anyway."

We were going to defend our intelligence when Burt Thomas, the cartoonist, dipped in his pocket and produced something.

"This is rather neat," he said mildly, "it is a little compass, see, with a revolving dial instead of an arrow, and the dial points to the North."

We demanded: "What do you, the most sedentary of men, traveling only between your office and your apartment house, want to be carrying a compass around for?"

"It's very handy in a bridge game," said Burt. "It shows who is North."

"But you don't play bridge," we blurted.

"No, I don't," conceded Mr. Thomas and busied himself lighting a long, lean cigar.

Mr. Lysinger speared us with an ice-pick eye and asked: "Do you know how to tell South on your wrist watch?"

"No," we admitted, "but I can generally tell what time it is if my watch runs."

"And you," snorted Mr. Lysinger, "write about Boy Scouts every week, and don't know how to tell South on your wrist watch!"

"How do you do it?" we asked, a-drool for information.

"You point the minute hand at the sun," said Mr. Lysinger, "and South is half way between where the minute hand is and where 12 o'clock is.

We munched a sandwich. We inquired:

"You mean, if the minute hand said it was 20 minutes to 12, and you pointed it at the sun, then South would be half way between 20 minutes of 12 and 12—or 10 minutes of 12?"

"Certainly not," Mr. Lysinger sniffed. "South would be at approximately 20 minutes past 11."

"Awk," we observed, and Mr. Lysinger elaborated: "You measure from the minute hand to 12 o'clock in a counter-clockwise direction."

"Oh," we said and bounced up. "Sorry," we added, "but I've got to leave—some work to do." With which we departed amidst cynical smiles. . . .

We have often noticed that when anyone learns something, he always wants to teach someone else. So:

We tried to show Cecil the Weecil how to tell South on a wrist watch, only he already knew. So we resorted to: "Burt Thomas has a compass."

"What does he want a compass for?" the Weecil gasped.

"I wouldn't know," we sighed. "Any more than I would know why so essentially a city product as Burt should insist on constantly bogging down his pants by lugging around a Boy Scout jack knife."

The Weecil sprang to his feet. A man of action is the Weecil. (We often pohemize about "Cecil the Weecil, powered by Diesel.")

"I'm going to ask questions," said he, and departed. Pretty soon he came back, bringing a paroxysm with him.

It appears that while Mr. Thomas politely refrained from saying so at the table, he does not think highly of Mr. Lysinger's method for telling South.

"It's too unreliable," said Mr. Thomas. "How can he tell where South is if there isn't any sun?"

The Weecil hesitantly suggested that possibly it would be more feasible to get a small oak tree and carry it around, it being well known that oaks have moss on the north side, and consequently, the opposite side would be South.

"No," Mr. Thomas shook his head, "that's not very practical either—

"An oak tree would be rather hard to get through a revolving door. The simplest method of locating South would be a duck and a cake of dry ice."

"A duck and a cake of dry ice?" stuttered the Weecil.

"Certainly," Mr. Thomas nodded. "With a duck and a cake of dry ice, you could tell South at any time, day or night."

"And how do you figure that out?" the Weecil pleaded.

"Why," Mr. Thomas was patience itself, "if you had a duck and a cake of dry ice, and you wanted to know South, you'd just set the duck on the cake of dry ice, and the duck would say, 'O-o! Winter!' and fly straight South."

SUPER EFFICIENCY

If the Milton's next-door-cottage neighbors have felt a faint restraint in the attitude of the Miltons this year, the following may explain it:

The neighbors stay much later at their cottage than the Miltons do at theirs. Also, they go up earlier in the spring. In fact, the Miltons never have been known to go to their place before the latter part of June, while the neighbors are in residence by June 15. Last spring, however, the Miltons drove up in May and were some what bewildered to find that the woven wire fence between their place and the neighbor's, had been carefully taken out and rolled up.

They could not understand the reason for that at all. But they left the fence that way, and asked the grocer in the nearby village if he happened to have noticed the way that fence had been taken up.

The grocer looked at them impassively, and said:

"Your neighbor took it out last October, like he always does, and, if I know anythin' about it, he'll have it back again before you get up here in June, like he always does."

"But why does he take it out?" goggled Mr. Milton.

"He's to the west of you, ain't he?" demanded the grocer, and when Milton agreed, the grocer snorted:

"So he takes down that wire fence when the leaves start fallin', so the wind will blow his leaves on your lawn an' he won't have to rake 'em up!"

SORT OF CORNERED

Maggie came traipsing in here to ask, "Do you like stories that aren't particularly funny, and haven't any particular point to them?"

We responded that the printed column must look as if we like that sort of story very much indeed, which seemed to be all the incentive Maggie needed:

"The other day," said she, "I was over in one of the big stores where they keep the cash-girl-and-parcels-wrapper in a sort of a little boarded-in compartment.

"The girl in this particular compartment was crying as if her heart would break.

"On the outside of the compartment were two saleswomen and a floor manager. The three of them were patting the girl on the shoulder and telling her to be brave. So—

"I asked the saleswoman waiting on me: 'Whatever is the matter with that poor girl? Has there been a death in her family?' And the saleswoman shrugged and answered:

" 'There really isn't anything the matter with her. She just thinks there is. There's a mouse in the compartment with her.' "

THAT'S SPELLING

Six-year-old Tommy Allen sat right up straight the first day of school when his teacher took up a pretty intricate subject, to wit, spelling.

Teacher asked the class in general this question:

"Can you tell me the use of spelling?"

Tommy brandished an eager hand. Teacher gave him the go sign, and Tommy came out with:

"The use of spelling is so you can spell to your wife or husband so the kids can't repeat it."

And while we're on the subject of s-p-e-l-l-i-n-g out words to b-a-m-b-o-o-z-l-e the young, this might be the spot to interject a radio-told story we've been urged to repeat:

Two neighbor ladies came over to call on Mrs. Jones the day she returned from the hospital. While the nurse was getting Mrs. Jones prettied up for this visit, the two women waited in the living room, with four-and-a-half-year-old Mamie Jones acting as hostess.

One of the woman studied Mamie's face for a while and then remarked to the other:

"She's not very p-r-e-t-t-y, is she?"

"No," said Mamie promptly, "but I'm very s-m-a-r-t."

STITCH IN TIME

Miss Amanda Ducknoodle was one of a carload of folks who have been doing some touring through the South—

She is a shy little spinster, very proper and aristocratic, who has one abiding fear in her life: That fire will break out in a hotel where she's staying.

The result of this phobia was that at each overnight stop on the trip we're discussing, the first thing Miss Amanda did on being assigned a room was to look over the fire-prevention situation, and to locate the nearest fire escape.

So, naturally, that was what she did when her group stopped in rather a smallish southern town and lodged in a distinctly ramshackle two-story inn, of cracker-box construction.

Miss Amanda took up the matter of fire hazards with the manager, who swelled up with Southern pride and responded:

"Madam, this hotel has stood here foh 50 years and, as you can see foh yeself, it sho' hasn't been burned down. In fact, there has never been a fiah."

Somehow these words didn't seem to comfort Miss Amanda as much as they should.

Which explains the fact that she'd no sooner been taken to a room on the second floor than she began looking for the fire escape.

The more she sought a fire escape without finding one, the more nervous and excited she became.

She even got to the point of opening unlocked doors along the corridor, hoping she could locate the room whence the fire escape sprouted downward.

Thus it happened that when she opened one door, she found herself facing a distinctly nude gentleman parked in a bathtub.

It was pretty hard to tell which of the twain was the more surprised.

Miss Amanda froze. So did the gent in the tub, a dripping sponge suspended in mid-air. They stared blankly at each other, and then Miss Amanda began getting embarrassed—

Probably no feminine face in all the world's hectic history has ever registered more of horror than that which etched itself into the meek little, shy little face of Miss Amanda Ducknoodle.

And still they stared at each other. Then Miss Amanda heard herself speaking and, due to the strain, she was speaking in a tone far from her normally mild murmur. In fact, spoke in a shriek, a cracked, excited shriek. She wailed:

"P-p-ardon me, but I'm looking for the fire escape!"

The gentleman in the tub blinked at her a moment more. Then he came astoundingly and aboundingly to life. Out of the tub he leapt.

Around his midst he draped a hasty towel. He spurted past Miss Amanda like a pumpkin seed squirted from boyish fingers. He went high-tailing it down the hall, bellowing "Fire!" at every bound. . . .

ADVERTISING SPECIALIST

An advertising friend of ours came back from some sort of a trip through the deep South with an experience he will be telling about for years to come:

At a hotel in a sleepy Southern town he was escorted to his room by a sleepy sort of superannuated bellhop—a man at least 50 years old.

When they reached the room the bell-boy inquired (and we are not going to try to imitate his dialect):

"What's your line of merchandise, Mister?"

"I'm an advertising man," came the answer, and the bell-hop immediately came to life.

"Is that so!" he exclaimed in excited tones. "Why I was an advertising man once myself but," and he sighed, "I had to give it up. It was too hard on me."

The Detroiter asked: "What was your line? Newspaper? Direct-by-mail? Or were you, perhaps, a contact man, or an account executive, or—"

"It was like this," came the bell-hop's answer, "it was about 30 years ago, and there was one of these here traveling hypnotists what used to travel from town to town, hypnotizin' the natives and scarin' some folks into crossin' their fingers. I did his advertising."

"Oh," said our advertising expert, "you went on ahead and gave him the old build-up?"

"Not exactly that," came the bell-hop's reply. "It was this-a-way:

"That hypnotizer useta drum up interest in his show in each town by hypnotizin' a man to sleep in the front window of the biggest store, and I was the man he put to sleep."

JOE LOUIS DIDN'T SEE

The chuckling that's going around town about the way in which Joe Louis can emit a remark as pungent verbally as that left of his is pungent in the ring, probably is the reason we found ourselves recalling an incident of 1940 in which we, obscurely, played a supporting role to that self-same Joe:

Due to the benevolence of the boss we had a crackerjack seat for the first World Series game played here that year.

When we eased into our seat we discovered a hulking pair of

shoulders ahead of us, topped mostly by a pork-pie hat. And in practically no time we'd found that the owner of both was Joe Louis.

With him was a chum, rather small and, as this incident developed, increasingly nervous:

The various proceedings on the diamond had taken their patterned course, to the point where the game would be starting in perhaps 10 minutes when we felt a tap on our shoulder. We turned, and there was a woman. Next her, a bug-eyed boy of perhaps 12 years old.

"Mister," the woman said, "my kid here wonders if Joe Louis will autograph this score card."

We said we'd see and leaning forward, tapped Louis on the shoulder. He turned slightly. We said:

"Joe, there's a kid back of me who wants your autograph on his score card."

Joe didn't say anything. He just reached out a hand as big as a ham, took the card, produced a pencil, no, come to think of it, we supplied him with a yellow newspaper pencil, and on that card he began to form his name. Well—

When he'd finished, we thanked him, and passed the card back to the woman, and immediately, three other cards came over our shoulder, with urgent requests for Louis' signature.

"Look," we said to him—and of course he didn't know us from Adam's off ox—"I'm sorry, but here are three other kids wanting autographs."

Joe didn't say anything. He merely took the score cards, and began putting his name on them.

And by then, the ball game was starting.

But it wasn't starting as far as Joe Louis was concerned.

By that time, score cards were being passed from all around that section of the grand stand, most of them, it seemed to an irritated us, through us.

And Joe kept signing.

At the end of two and a half innings, Joe was still putting his name on programs. We don't think he had seen a single play.

And still he had a stack of cards to autograph.

It was well into the third inning, with Joe still writing, that his next-seat chum said:

"Hey, Joe. You've done enough of that, now. You haven't seen any of the ball game. Come on, Joe, that's enough signing."

Joe kept right on soberly autographing. He answered, and the answer was meant for his chum, not for us, nor for publication, and in a shyly apologetic tone:

"Aw," said Joe, "the kids sort of like to have me write my name for 'em."

He finished the last of the stack of score cards around the middle of the fourth inning. Then, he went home.

PAUL REVERE BEEN HERE?

Far on the eastern fringe of Grosse Pointe dwells a man who is not only deeply interested in horses, but can afford to own horses, which is a horse of an entirely different color.

One day he came upon a saddle-horse he yearned to buy. Whether this was a case of green pastures or not, the fact is he found this steed out in that happy-hunting ground of horsemen which seems to start around Grand River and the Six Mile road and fan out toward Northville.

After some covert inquiries, he found that this horse was owned by the jovial head of a riding stable in that area, so he phoned from his far-East home to the stable, and asked the riding-master if he wanted to sell that horse.

The upshot was that early the next afternoon, our hero whom we'll call Mr. Pointer for reasons that may develop as this report develops, hied himself by car from his home to that stable, 'way out Grand River. He got there around 2 P. M. and immediately he and the horse's owner went into their David Harum act.

The horse's owner brought out a quart of whiskey, and poured out a couple of man, or horseman-sized stirrup-cups, sort of to lubricate the bargaining. And as the tempo of the bargaining went up, the level of the likker went down. In fact:

By 6 P. M. the bottle was empty, and the deal was almost sealed.

The owner opened another quart, and the two of them got down to the finer points of their discussion and it does seem to us as if Mr. Pointer got the better of the bargain because, for his price, he managed to get:

One (1) saddle-horse.

One (1) blanket.

One (1) saddle and

One-and-one-half (1½) pints of (free) drinking likker.

With mere business out of the way, the former owner and the new owner settled down for a chummy chat about horsemanship in general, punctuating their remarks with a few drinks. And suddenly, it was 11 P. M.

The former owner abruptly said: "Look. You got the horse, and here it is 11 o'clock, and I haven't any trailer to haul him 30 miles from here to Grosse Pointe, and you said you wanted to show him to your wife first thing in the morning. What're we goin' to do?"

Mr. Pointer considered that point owlishly for some time. Then he stated firmly:

"I'll ride 'im home, m'shelf, right now!"

Such forthrightness appealed to the former owner. He yelled for one of his hostlers, and the hostler proceeded to bring out the horse, insert the bit in his mouth, and put on the saddle blanket. Then:

He put the saddle on the blanket and, with, it must be admitted, the aid of the former owner, he put Mr. Pointer on the saddle.

And thus began the midnight ride of Paul Revere ('46 model).

The horse was as loath as is any horse to leave home base, so Mr. Pointer had to exert some pressure to get him under way. But under way he got, at a rather reluctant stroll. And the hour was 11 P. M.

Mr. Pointer rather foggily summed up the surroundings and managed to find Grand River avenue, that throbbing thorofare slitting straight to the pulsing heart of Dynamic Detroit (with the sun in your eyes both ways).

Thereafter, to the increasing astonishment of the increasingly sparse traffic on that main artery, Mr. Pointer's horse klop-klopped lazily toward downtown.

Eventually, he reached Woodward Avenue, and poked down past that interesting edifice, rookery, snuggery, and pigeon roost known as the City Hall.

By then, even the pigeons had gone to bed, and few were the citizens left to stare at this Mr. Revere who was going so slowly it's just as well that no British were coming.

In time, Mr. Pointer and steed reached Jefferson, where they executed an elaborate column left, no, we mean left wheel, and set out along Jefferson, going East and East and Always East.

It was 5 A. M. when Mr. Pointer finally rode his new steed up to his home. He decided it would be wiser not to rouse his wife from her slumbers, so he put the horse in the stable and stumbled into the house.

That is about all there is to this story except to add two smallish points:

When Mr. Pointer came to in the morning, and had sufficiently reduced the size of his head so he could remember, he hurried to the stable and found that his horse was none the worse for wear.

And about then, Mr. Pointer remembered that throughout the 30 miles of his whiskey-inspired horseback ride, he had had a high old time sneering at every policeman and Scout Car he saw because he was smugly aware that no matter how tight he might be they couldn't arrest him for driving while drunk.

HIS ATTITUDE

As the murder trial got under way, the attorney for the defendant began scanning the prospective jurors with what he hoped was an x-ray eye.

He was particularly impressed by the friendly, portly appearance of prospective Juror No. 3.

The attorney lounged over to him and started a series of

innocuous questions, all of which were pleasantly answered, if in English that might have brought a frown to the pristine brow of a purist.

Finally he asked:

"Do you believe in capital punishment?"

"I certainly do not," snorted the juror. "Why send 'em to Lansing? I believe in hangin' 'em right here in Detroit."

HIS BRIGHT BROAD SMILE

This is a true story that we have treasured for a good many years. Many a time we have wanted to print it, because implicit in it there seemed to be so much more humanity than anything we had been able to exhume during 24 hours of digging, yet—

Always we knew we could not use the story and now, we are sorry to say, we can.

With this preliminary, we'll go ahead, pausing only to suggest that this story may mean more to those men and women who know how hard it is, out of a small pay envelope, to get even a few dollars to the good—those reluctant, those restless, those winged dollars that don't want to stay saved, even for a purpose that is fine:

Jerry came home to supper that evening, not from a position, but from a job.

His wife greeted him at the door with that matchless smile of hers, and yet—it was not exactly her usual smile. There was something of triumph in it; something of having achieved.

And it was surprising to see so deep a smile on her face, because that was a Monday night and Monday night usually found the wifely smile stretched thin:

Wash day and a balky washing machine; a fractious mechanism that, over the churning years, had taken on a malevolent personality of its own; a tendency to limp and sulk and be grouchy, like some humans who have passed the prime of life and who do things they really don't intend to do.

Jerry greeted his wife's smile with his own broad grin—the grin that had endeared him to hundreds and then—

He sniffed, as a good-hearted husband should sniff, if his wife is a good cook, and he is hungry. And he said: "You got something good for dinner? A surprise?"

"Yes," she nodded. "I really have a surprise."

So Jerry went to brush up, leaving the bathroom door open because it was nice to hear her humming as she clattered the dishes around in that friendly symphony that is music indeed to the ears of a man who is tired, and, secretly, very happy—happy with the thought of little privations long endured that joy might come to someone else.

He called: "How'd the washing machine behave today?" and he winked at himself in the mirror, because the kitchen symphony had stopped.

"Terrible," she seethed. "It stuck half way through, and I had to do the rest by hand and I do wish you wouldn't use your handkerchiefs to polish your shoes or whatever you do with them!"

"Yes, dear," said Jerry, as he had been saying for 20 years.

Again the symphony struck up, and his wife called: "Hurry, dear. Dinner's on the table."

"Yes, dear," he answered and added: "So that old machine made trouble again?"

"Oh," rather shortly, from the kitchen. "Let's not talk about it. I do wish we had enough money to get a new one but—if we can save enough—you've got to have a new suit. . . . Hurry up, Slowpoke."

"Yes, dear," and Jerry gave his grinning reflection a parting, owlish wink. . . .

When a woman has some news to break, she seldom breaks it right away. She likes to save it, to savor it, to build it up.

This is a fact all husbands understand, and understanding husbands undergo.

Jerry told the little things that had happened during his day, out in the wide world, not shut in the house with a sulky washing machine. It was into the middle of dessert that she tossed:

"I've got a surprise for you, Jerry. I made a good deal today."

"You did?" he asked.

"Yes," she nodded. "You know that old gray suit of yours? The one that's been hanging in the back of your closet for two years?"

"Yes, dear," Jerry said, and his hand tightened on his spoon.

"Well," she glowed, "a stray junk-man came along and I sold him that suit for two dollars. Two whole dollars. And we'll use those two dollars toward your new suit!"

Jerry spooned something into his mouth. He gulped. He said: "Gee! You sold that old suit for two dollars. Why, that's wonderful! You're a good business woman, my dear."

And he beamed at her—that bright, broad smile of his.

And not then, nor later, nor ever, did he tell her that in the watch pocket of that old gray suit, sold to a junk-man he could never locate, was $90 he had saved, a dollar or so at a time out of those reluctant, those restless, those winged dollars, that he might, that very week, buy her a brand new washing machine. . . .

NOT SO GOLDEN

Daniel Jordan, eight-year-old possessor of that remarkable musical gift known as "absolute pitch," was called from his bedroom the other evening by his father, Cliff, to display his talent to the PTA Fathers' Quartet, assembled at the Jordan home for a practice session.

Danny appeared, in pajamas and bathrobe, listened to each note his father struck on the piano and, with unhesitating accuracy, called it by name.

Then, at his father's instruction, he perched on a chair, prepared to listen to the next quartet number and to tell each singer whether he was on-pitch or off-key.

It seems perfectly sensible to us that, with such an audience, the quartet started out rather raggedly and galloped through the song. But you will be glad to know that they finished in an appropriate tie, with Danny listening intently, his eyes closed, and a pained expression over-shadowing his freckles.

The quartet slued its collectively nervous eyes toward Danny when silence had descended.

Danny looked at the floor. Then he beckoned the baritone.

Danny looked at him a long moment and then whispered:

"Would you like to come up to my room and see my match-cover collection?"

CORN OR CORN

After Monday's broadcast, during which we found ourselves, somewhat to our astonishment, rendering James Whitcomb Riley's "Frost is on the punkin," we came back here to the Youth Center.

We kept muttering lines from that bucolic classic, with considerable emphasis on two, the one about "it sets my heart a clickin' like the tickin' of a clock," which is a nice melody, and that superb picture-line:

"The husky, rusty rustle of the tossels of the corn."

That the other members of the Youth Center didn't know what we were being so emphatic about, we didn't realize; nor did we measure the exact number of decibels we were putting into our elocution until:

Pedro, who should have been more immersed in his work, paused to inquire solicitously:

"Jack, what sort of corn are you talking about? The kind that grows or the kind you write?"

DESCRIPTIVE

ALCIB says that five-year-old Lucy accompanied her mother on a shopping expedition. Mother met a friend and stopped to chat.

Mother's friend, polite and tactful, wished to include Lucy in the conversation.

"What are you doing that's interesting?" she asked.

"I'm going to dancing school," stated Lucy.

"Oh, that's nice," smiled Friend. "So you're learning to dance."

"Well," said Lucy frankly, "I've just started. I'm learning to bow."

"Learning to bow?" parroted the friend and Lucy responded:

"Yes. The girls bend their knees and the boys bend their stummicks."

ONLY FIVE

Dorothy Baldwin, a becoming young matron who dwells in the suburbs, returned to her husband, Don, and Barby, their 5-year-old daughter, from a trip to town, in a beatific state of triumph.

Dorothy had spent a goodly portion of her allowance on a new hat—one of those black, feathery, frilly, veilly affairs.

Naturally, she was no sooner in the house than she proceeded to model it for Don and Barby.

Don, being a husband, was the perfect stoic but Barby burst out into resounding bellows of the heartiest mirth. Finally, she controlled herself enough to gasp:

"Oh, Mommy! You just bought that for a joke on Daddy and me!"

AMBASSADOR'S REASON

During their recent vacation trip that took them to Washington, D. C., Mr. and Mrs. J. L. S. Scrymgeour were the guests of the new British Ambassador, Lord Inverchapel, for lunch.

His Lordship turned out to be an affable and amiable gentleman, with a slight trend toward the unconventional, if the beginning of the luncheon is any criterion:

He was no more than seated before he unfolded his linen napkin and somberly inspected its edges.

Sure enough, two or three threads stuck out.

His Lordship fished in a pocket and came out with a cigaret lighter. He flicked it into flame and while the British Embassy butler stood austerely behind him, and the Scrymgeour eyes were a trifle startled, His Lordship proceeded, cautiously, to burn away those protruding threads—without injuring the napkin. Then,

He turned to Mrs. Scrymgeour and inquired, courteously:

"Have you examined your napkin yet?"

When Mrs. Scrymgeour confessed she hadn't, he assisted her in unfolding it and behold, several loose ends extended therefrom.

With a polite "Pardon me," His Excellency appropriated her napkin and, again bringing his trusty lighter ablaze, he singed the threads from that one.

"You see," he explained, "there should never be threads on napkins, but there usually are, and it always annoys me to see folks plucking at those threads. If you pull a thread, it is likely to ravel the napkin. It is much more sensible to burn them off."

With which observation, His Lordship settled to his lunch.

DOWAGER DID IT

As many a wife-meeting husband will attest, the parking situation on Washington Boulevard behind the David Whitney Building is something to shudder about.

He who double-parks is double-dammed. He who tries actually to get into a space along that stretch of curbing probably can't make it because he's so paralyzed with astonishment at finding a place. However:

Earlier in the day, sometimes parking spots do come along, and toward one of them, recently, headed a limousine about as long as a battleship.

Behind the wheel was a uniformed chauffeur, approximately the size of a jockey. On the back seat was a great big woman, a veritable Amazon, with a stern profile, jutting and patrician. The profile of a person who takes such a showcase for granted. The chauffeur got to the open space—a pretty short space for such a bandwagon but, nevertheless, a space.

He began the laborious, prolonged and, in this case, unsuccessful process of warping his liner into dock. Back and forth he shunted, with much spinning of the wheel, and certain movements of his lips.

Back and forth and forth and back, seven, eight, nine times.

At that moment, the passenger came to life. She grabbed the speaking tube and addressed the chauffeur. The car came to a stop.

The dowager flung open the rear left-hand door, stepped to the pavement, yanked open the front left-hand door, practically tweaked the astounded chauffeur from his seat, climbed in, grabbed the wheel and, in four neat zoops, she parked the car parallel with the curb.

Then, out she flounced, her high heels practically striking sparks from the street. She stared bleakly at the chauffeur and "boob!" she boomed at him as she swished away from there.

HABIT BRINGS A SHOCK

Good habits, there be, and habits that are bad, and to either, a person, or a twain, can become well-shackled slaves.

Take Mr. and Mrs. Dinglehoofer and their morning dog-walking:

Dinglehoofer arises first, and gets his own breakfast. Then he takes the dog for a bit of a walk, and leaves him in the side yard.

When, some half hour later, Mrs. Dinglehoofer puts in her downstairs appearance, she goes to the grade door, opens it and calls for this dog, who doubtless feels himself disgraced because he's usually called "Baby."

The other morning, strictly to schedule, Dinglehoofer was up, breakfasted and gone, with the dog in the side yard. And—

Strictly to schedule, Mrs. Dinglehoofer klip-klopped down stairs in a somewhat scanty nightie and negligee.

Automatically, she arrived at the grade door, and with the practice of months of habit, she swung it partly open, calling, cooingly:

"Come in, Baby. Come on in."

Then she glanced up and found herself staring into the staring eyes of the new milkman.

AN ORCHID IS

When you're mothering two small children and doing all your own scrubbing, corsages, particularly orchids, are Events, says Mrs. Shirley.

Sally received one from her husband's genial boss on the morning of the day she was to leave for New York on a long anticipated vacation. But. . . .

The orchid arrived, to find Sally unpacking because, as so often happens in this weary world, both children were sniffly and feverish; so much so that the trip to New York had to be postponed.

Sally sadly put the corsage in the refrigerator and, as the day wore on, what with wiping noses and squeezing juices and taking higher temperatures, Sally's spirits dropped lower and lower.

Next day, the children were worse. And each time Sally took more oranges from the refrigerator, she stared at that Orchid.

The following day, they were better but still requiring care.

And that is the reason why, that day, she grimly greeted the milkman, the astonished bread man, the postman, and finally, her husband, with that orchid pinned to the shoulder of her house-dress. . . .

HE BUTTED IN

Peppy Eppy reports that she was in a bakery when in came two women, one young and one middle-aged, and immediately went into a huddle with the baker himself, about a wedding cake.

They finished the specifications as to size and the number of layers, and then began concerning themselves with the top decorations.

The baker spread out on the counter before them half a dozen different combinations of bells, flowers, miniature brides and grooms. The women debated and discussed, as is proper in arriving at a momentous decision.

Suddenly they became aware that a burly gent had edged nearer and nearer until his chin was practically resting on their adjacent shoulders.

Their chatter stopped abruptly and they both stared at him.

"Don't mind me, ladies," he reassured them, "my wife and I eloped and I just wanted to see what the hell I missed."

MELLOW AS A BELLOW

Pity the poor mother of growing youths who's married to an Old Moss Back! At least, that is the plea of a mother who signs herself "Forty and I don't look it."

"I have one son 16 and one 17," she writes, "and one 22, who is at the University of Michigan and, in the words of my offspring, I am very much on the ball, because:

"I go to Ann Arbor to football games, to baseball games, and to basketball games. When I am not going to Ann Arbor to ball games, I go, here in Detroit, with my sons and the Old Moss Back, to football games, to baseball games, and to basketball games.

"I also listen to atrocious music with an attentive ear and have been known to murmur, 'That's in the groove.' But now I am a little miffed:

"Last Sunday, I started for church wearing a new pair of loafers—

"Perhaps loafers are not exactly the proper shoes for such an occasion, but I was going directly out afterward to do some Red Feather work.

"As I reached the door—the Old Moss Back already was out front in the car—those two sons took one look at my loafers and then looked at each other in horror.

" 'Mother,' gasped Seventeen, 'you can't go like that!' "

Mrs. Mother says she bridled at the objection "and I asked him why not. I said:

" 'I'm not going to take another pair of shoes in the car and I am not going to go pounding pavements getting contributions, with high heels on.'

" 'Oh, I didn't mean that,' said Seventeen. 'I mean that your loafers don't shine.'

" 'Shine?' I demanded, looking at their lustrous brown, 'they certainly do —' but my voice trailed off because the two of them had gone into a huddle, while the Old Moss Back beeped the horn outside.

" 'Sorry, Mother,' Seventeen finally said, after they had dug in their pockets and compared contents, 'we haven't any nice new pennies, like there should be, but we've got four dimes,' and before I could say a word, the two of them were down on their knees, inserting two dimes in the slit at the tongue of each loafer."

Mrs. Mother admits she was pretty well bewildered by the time they straightened up and Seventeen said:

" 'There, Moms, now your loafers have a sparkle to them.'

" 'Sure,' agreed Sixteen, 'they shine.'

" 'Yep, Moms,' nodded Seventeen, 'now you look sharp.'

"And Sixteen asserted, 'You bet, Moms. You're mellow as a bellow,' whatever that means. And just then, the Old Moss Back outside really leaned on the horn.

"So I hurried out along the front walk, and I took a quick look at my feet, and to tell you the truth, I rather liked what the twinkle of those four dimes did to my ankles.

"But I guess the Old Moss Back didn't. He stared out of the window at me as I approached, and demanded:

" 'What in tunket is the matter with your feet?'

"So I said, rather loftily: 'They're oke. I look mellow as a bellow.'

"And he gave me the sourest sort of stare and snarled:

" 'There's no fool like an old fool,' and wouldn't speak to me all the way to church."

HER WAY

She would not want her name used, nor would we divulge her address—this gold star mother who is quietly remaking her life after the death of her son, over Austria.

His room is just as he left it, when he went, with level eyes and squared shoulders, away from home to take his share in giving us all the chance to make ours a better country.

Yes, his room is just as he left it. And there were those days and weeks and months when it was difficult for her to enter. And then she had an idea:

"What better memorial could there be to my son," she thought, "than, in these days of rooming shortages, to make my boy's room a Memorial to him?"

And that is what she has done. Whenever she hears of a veteran who is temporarily homeless; or of a veteran's wife who can find no place to go, she opens to the veteran, or the wife, her son's Memorial Room.

GRAND'MERE WAS A PROBLEM

Russell Barnes took time from his work of reporting UN activities in New York to let us know about an incident that happened in France during his recent stay that created considerable commotion, and hadn't been solved at the time Russ left Paris.

A French family decided the time had come to move from a small village back to the family home in Paris. The man of the family arranged that the household goods should go by truck, but that the members of the family should descend upon Paris by train.

This seemed perfectly sensible until the morning of departure when, with the truck partly loaded, and the folks just about to go to the train, Grandmother, "Grand'mere," took the bit in her teeth.

She said she definitely was not going to Paris by train.

She said she did not like the trains and she did not trust trains. She preferred, she declared, to ride in the truck.

In vain were pleas advanced. Grand'mere was adamant.

Finally, with much gallic gesticulating, they boosted Grand'-mere's favorite rocker into the truck and installed a grim-jawed Grand'mere in the rocker. Well—

In time, the rest of the family reached Paris, and the home from which they'd been separated so long. There was not much to do but wait for the truck to arrive and, eventually it did.

It larruped up in front of the house, and out sprang the driver. He dashed up the front steps, and even an amateur at Frenchmen could see something was wrong with him.

The driver hammered on the front door, and when it was opened, dashed in. His eyes were well bugged out as the family gathered around him.

"That Grand'mere," he gasped, "she died. I didn't know it. I just looked back in the truck and there she was, dead, in her chair."

With one accord the bereaved family and the trucker swung open the front door and dashed down to see for themselves. Only, it didn't do them much good. The truck had been stolen.

PREMONITION!

Mrs. Albert of Belleville says that recently, beginning with the early morning, she had a premonition that her husband was buying something for her.

"I kept thinking and thinking about it," she reports. "And the more I thought the more I built it up. Finally, I decided it must be either chocolate candy, or nylons. Well—

"When he came home that evening he acted very mysterious, and finally he said:

" 'Honey, I bought you a little present today.'

"I had to control myself," Mrs. Albert smiled, "to keep from telling him my woman's intuition had told me he'd done just that. I acted very excited, and I could almost taste those chocolates, or see the sheen of the nylons. . . .

"He went back out the back door and came in with a package and handed it to me. And I guess you can guess how hurriedly I opened it. Then:

"I laughed and laughed until Friend Hubby pretty gruffly wanted to know what was so funny. But it was funny because what he'd bought me was a sponge mat to make kneeling easier while I scrubbed the floor."

HER DEFENSE

Mrs. W. A. Shelly is still amused over a sight she beheld at the last football game held in Ann Arbor.

As she and her husband were returning from the stadium, blending with the mob moving toward parked cars and railroad trains, she heard someone call "Look out," so she looked:

A path led across a lawn. But that path wasn't being used.

On the lawn stood a belligerent looking lady, her eyes glaring. She was holding a garden hose, out of which was spurting a full head of water. This stream swooshed right across the entrance to that inviting short-cut. And no one was taking it.

Her silent system was working a good deal better than a "Please Keep Off the Grass" sign, Mrs. Shelly says, and adds that this proprietorial lady has been on the job every single game-day Saturday. She was even there, squirting that hose during the rain in which the Army-Michigan game ended.

FIELD MOUSE FIELD-DAY

With the first sharp nip of frost, each fall, many a harried housewife screams at discovering she is hostess to a drove of uninvited guests—

Little friendly field mice decide it's high time to move indoors for the winter.

This fact came forcefully home to Mrs. Gwen the other morning when she found her house was infested with at least two mice.

Since Gwen is personally squeamish about mice, she called her sturdy husband into conference and he forthwith set two traps.

Yesterday morning, just as he was leaving for the office, he called upstairs to her that he'd caught and dispatched one, "but," he said, "here's a strange one—I can't find the other trap. Maybe the mouse carried it away, hah, hah, hah," on which high note of humor, he departed.

When Mrs. Gwen came downstairs, she discovered the family dog, Towser, was behind the davenport, deeply interested in the hot-air register, set flush with the floor. She went over to inspect and her inspection ended in a small shriek:

The other trap was wrong-side up, flat on the register, and down through the register dangled a very lively mouse, caught by the tail in the trap.

Gwen frantically wondered what she was going to do. She couldn't leave that mouse a-dangle, and she certainly wasn't going to hoist it out of the register. She—and then came the thought.

She phoned the nearest police station and to the gruff voice answering, she reported:

"I need some help. I'm in a lot of trouble."

"Burglars?" demanded the voice.

"No. Mice," Gwen burbled. "I've got a mouse in a trap and—"

"Lady," said the voice, "we got a crime wave and I am very sorry, but we just ain't got the equipment to send over a Scout Car and take a mouse out of a trap for you. You better just let it lay until your husband comes home."

"But," Gwen wailed, "this mouse is alive."

Silence broadened before the voice replied: "We still ain't got police to take mice out of traps. Sorry," and click! went the phone.

Gwen was pretty mad, and into her anger came the yap of Towser and a definite squeak from that pendulous mouse. Something had to be done.

At that moment she heard a cheery male voice raised in song in the back yard. Gwen rushed thitherward. It was the garbage man, joyously juggling cans.

"Mister," Gwen called, "are you afraid of mice?"

The garbageer cautiously set down the can he was wrestling, ceased his rendition of "Doin' What Comes Naturally," and inquired: "Am I afraid of what?"

"Mice," said Gwen.

"No, Mam," the garbageer responded grimly. "I ain't afraid of mice. What's the matter?"

Gwen plunged into her story, ending with "and that mouse is still dangling down the register right now."

"Hmmm," observed the garbageer, eyeing her a bit oddly, and "Okay," said he, bringing his vivid personality into the living room. "I will be doggone," he declared, "there is a mouse!"

With which observation he lifted trap, tail, and mouse, the latter wriggling so frantically that Gwen heard herself saying: "The poor little thing, don't hurt it."

The garbageer bowed politely, remarking: "You are just like all the other ladies, Madam, You are tender-hearted. However, he is sort of a cute little cuss. It does seem a shame to kill him."

"Don't," Gwen begged.

The garbageer went into a brown study, the mouse still squirming and squeaking. Then the garbageer's face split into a triumphant grin.

"I got it," he crowed, and departed for the back door, toting trap, tail, and mouse.

Gwen followed. The garbageer approached his truck. He held the mouse over the side and unsnapped the trap.

The garbageer tossed the trap on the back porch and climbed in the driver's seat. He beamed at Gwen. He observed:

"There Lady. You are rid of your mouse, and boy! with a whole loada garbage to pick from, that there field mouse is gonna have himself a field day."

The garbageer ground his chariot into gear. He added:

"You know, Lady, I'm awful glad there was a mouse. To tell the truth, I sorta smelled a rat."

IMAGINATION

Tommy, who's 2.5 years old, accompanied his dad and mother when they went to visit a man with whom Tommy's dad was in the Army.

Being a perfectly normal youngster, Tommy was brimming with curiosity about this house with which he was unacquainted. He finally pointed to the door of Friend's clothespress. "What's in there?" he demanded, and Friend replied, "That's where I keep my horse."

With that, Friend swung the door wide open and asked: "Don't you see my horse?"

"No," Tommy answered, "but I sure can smell him."

CLERK'S REACTION

Mrs. Michael Bloy says the woman who was the center of the following brief incident didn't get back to normal for quite a while:

She was in a crowded grocery store, with hurried clerks running in all directions.

She felt she had a right to a little service, especially since all she wanted was a quarter of a pound of shelled walnuts—and she was standing at the counter where she could see them in a glass jar. So:

She flagged a passing clerk with: "Are you the one who waits on the nuts?"

"And how, Lady. And how," he blurted as he spurted past.

NOT ALL THE DANDELIONS

Come the bright warm days of next spring, with the dandelions popping their tousled yellow heads out of Elderly Nelson's lawn—Mrs. Nelson is going to think that Nelson, arch-enemy of dandelions, is losing his stuff:

"I am going to manage it," said Nelson, "in such a way that there will be at least one dandelion in full bloom, all the time, right on my de-dandelioned lawn."

This deviation from the death-to-dandelions principle that has activated Nelson for many a long, lush year, is something Mrs. Nelson is going to have to figure out for herself, unless she happens to read this column and, wives being wives, we rather hope she does. With which prefatory note:

"Some weeks ago," said Nelson, "I was walking in the factory where I am employed—my job allows for considerable roaming around—and I came to the back of the plant.

"A group of men were dismantling a temporary building there and, since I am an expert observer of steam-shovels, or bulldozers, or other efforts of that sort, I naturally paused to see how the work was coming. And then I noticed two men."

Elderly Nelson smiled and went on: "One of them, I knew. A chap about my own age, named George.

"Teamed up with him was a young fellow, maybe 27 years old, I didn't know. But—

"I took a second look at him because he was stripped to the waist, and as brown as coffee.

"He was wearing a sort of a baseball cap with a long peak, tilted straight up from a shock of black hair. And he had a swell pair of shoulders and his face was sort of grim and unsmiling.

"George and this young man were working away with punch bars, taking down 2-by-4s, and things of that sort, and the young man was easing the work for George.

"It finally dawned on me that maybe this chap was George's son, who had been in the Army a long time, so I asked a man who happened to be handy and he said, yes, that was George's son."

Elderly Nelson said to this informant: "It's sort of nice to see a father and son working together, isn't it?"

And the informant answered, "Yeah, and there's sort of an odd story connected with that young fellow. . . .

"Years ago, when he was only four or maybe five years old, he heard his mother saying how much she loved flowers, so this little lad went out in the vacant lot next door and came back and said:

" 'Look, Movver. I've brought you some flowers.'

"And what he had was a bunch of dandelions. And his mother? She reached down and picked him up and hugged him and told him it was—and it was the truth—it was the most beautiful bouquet she'd ever had. Well—

"From that time on, during the dandelion season, whenever that lad gave his mother a present, there was always one dandelion with it, saying its special word of love. Well—"

Elderly Nelson's informant continued: "So that chap grew to manhood, and the Second World War came along and it wasn't long before he was in the Army.

"He got to be a captain, because he had what it takes. And his letters were the bright spots for George and his wife, and then—

"His letters stopped coming. And the days lagged by, and the time came when we didn't ask George any more if he'd heard from the boy—that time did come, you know, to many a friend. But—

"One day in the cold of December, when the strain was almost beyond enduring, George had a phone call from his wife. A letter had come. She couldn't open it.

"George drove home fast. And there was the letter—only, it wasn't in the boy's handwriting. Just a letter with an APO number.

"George grabbed it, and slit it along the top, and it fell out of his hands on the living room table, and something fell out of the envelope:

"A dandelion. A rumpled, bedraggled, war-worn dandelion.

"And the boy's mother sank down in a chair, and there were the stars of heaven in her eyes, and peace in the way she folded her hands. . . .

"George got the letter unfolded. It was from an Army nurse. A nice cheery letter. It said the boy was getting along fine. He was going to be all right. Then she wrote:

" 'He's getting, now, to that stage of convalescence where he is practically bossy. For example: For some reason, he absolutely insisted that I go out and pick a dandelion and enclose it in this letter.' "

WHY STORM WINDOWS ARE STORM WINDOWS

The reason storm windows are called "storm windows" is because of the family storm they always cause when they're put on, only we think such a storm is but a tempest in a teapot. . . .

Sunday was Mrs. Mama's birthday and storm window-putting-on day, and she wasn't fully well, so we suggested, directly after church, that she go to bed, while Son Seventeen and we served as food-bearers, Florence Nightingales, and such.

"But I can't go to bed," Mrs. Mama sighed, "you'd never get those storm windows on without me to supervise."

We shot a wily glance at Seventeen and cooed: "You command by remote control, and we'll get 'em on in fine shape." Mrs. Mama said:

"You have to wash the house windows, and the storm windows, and you have to get the right windows on the right windows, and you know perfectly well that—"

"Lady," we said indignantly, "I'll take care of everything. You take a rest."

Mrs. Mama went to bed. Seventeen eyed us. We both eyed the clock. "Let's go," we said.

"It's cold out there," said Seventeen.

"It's always cold when you put up storm windows," we snorted. "That's why you put up storm windows. Let's get going."

Seventeen began collecting pails, brushes, squeegees, cloths, and his energy.

We went out on the screened porch and began to wash windows. Our fingers turned the normal mortuary blue. But we washed windows. And when they, and the house windows were dry, we said:

"We'll get the upstairs ones on first."

We got 'em on, with Mrs. Mama giving advice. Then we descended and looked at the Real Job:

The columnistic house is blessed with five huge windows downstairs. Four are in the living room, the fifth in the dining room. But for some unknown reason—there are only four storm windows.

"What windows do these go on?" demanded Seventeen.

"You know very well where they go," we grunted. "Three go on the living room. The fourth goes on the dining room window."

"Why don't they all go on the living room?" demanded Seventeen.

"Because," we groused, "the window that faces the porch is protected by the screen of the porch. Come on."

Seventeen grabbed one of those big windows. "Look out," we wailed. "Easy with that, it's made of glass."

"Wumph," said Seventeen, and swung it around casually. He can swing anything around casually, including the house. He is five feet eleven and weighs 185 and believes that Muscle Will Do It.

We got the living room windows on. But difficulties arrived with the one for the dining room. It didn't want to fit.

"I'll fix it," said Seventeen and, before we could even bleat, he ducked into the shrubbery and came up with his ace in the hole—a croquet mallet. He began hammering the window-frame home.

Craack! And the top section splintered. Out fell a nice oblong piece about the shape, and size of Grosse Ile. "I wonder what made it do that?" puzzled Seventeen.

We said: "We won't mention this to mother until tomorrow. She doesn't feel well."

"And when we do," said Seventeen, "WE won't."

As we slid into our topcoat Monday morning we called up to Mrs. Mama: "There was a little mishap with one of those downstairs windows yesterday. It sort of, er, cracked."

Mrs. Mama came downstairs fast. We whistled like going past a graveyard and got the front door open.

"It's a great big break," Mrs. Mama announced.

"But," we soothed, "it is way up at the top of the window where it won't show."

Seventeen came downstairs, rolled an eye at us, and went in the kitchen.

"It's a big break," Mrs. Mama repeated.

"Okay," we grumbled. "But we did our best. The doggone window wouldn't fit. I guess it's warped."

"That's not what's warped," said Mrs. Mama. "You put that storm window on the wrong window. It goes on the other living room window. We never had a storm window in the dining room in our lives."

"That's what I told him," said Seventeen, the big traitor. He may have said more but we were on our way to work.

MAN BITES DOG

The Rev. Al Perry was not particularly surprised when he learned that a tiff had developed in the home of two young folks he joined in matrimony a couple of months ago.

The Reverend Al is seasoned enough to know that a spat is bound to spatter tears and recriminations around a brand new home. Anyway—

After the bride and groom really had battled, the groom abruptly got up from the living room and stamped into the bedroom.

There, he could be heard exhuming a suitcase from the wardrobe.

Mrs. Bride listened, and finally tiptoed to the well-slammed door. She opened it and peeked in. Mr. Groom was very busy hurling stuff into that suitcase.

"D-d-darling," she quavered, "where are you going?"

"I'm not going anywhere," Mr. Groom blared, "these are your clothes I'm packing."

NURSIE TO A BULL FIDDLE

Herewith is the story of the hockey player who inadvertently became nursemaid to a bull fiddle.

Some time ago, Jack Adams, the genial if choleric Brain behind Detroit's Red Wings, decided to ship Leslie Douglas, a center, to the Indianapolis hockey club.

So Douglas was on his way, little recking what was going to come along to wreck his aplomb.

All he had in mind as he went to Indianapolis was the thought of making a good center, and the fact that he would return to Detroit on Monday to collect Mrs. Douglas and take her back to

Indianapolis with him.

At approximately the time Douglas reported in Indianapolis, Sonja Henie and all her chicks departed that city for their current stand at Olympia, in Detroit.

And somehow, in the hurry of moving from Indianapolis to Detroit, there was a bit of absent-mindedness on the part of one of Sonja's musicians.

He, the bass-viol player, forgot his bull fiddle.

Much was the excitement in Sonja's orchestra when the fiddle player found he had no fiddle to fid.

Something drastic had to be done because you just don't step up and substitute a piccolo, for example, for a bull fiddle. So—

Arrangements were made to crate that fiddle and put it on a plane and fly it to Detroit, but—

Woe is us (and Sonja), the airplane line said that the fiddle was far too big a thing for a hostess to fiddle around with. No, sir! said the officials, that can't go unaccompanied!

At this point, the sorrows of Sonja, her musical director, and bull fiddler came to the kindly ears of the Olympia management, which is always ready (adv.) to Serve.

Olympia remembered that Douglas was in Indianapolis, and returning to Detroit so—why not have Douglas double in brass?

Which is why Douglas found himself aboard the plane, holding seven feet of fiddle in his lap.

Douglas shepherded the fiddle to Detroit all right, but upon getting out, he banged up against an occupational hazard of all bull fiddlers:

You not only have to learn how to play one of the doggone things but you have to learn how to be its platonic consort.

You can't very well fold up a bass viol. It has a shape of its own and prefers to retain its shape. And despite the depths of soulful music it can send, a bull fiddle is as clumsy as a cow.

Douglas toted the fiddle from the plane—"waltzed" is probably a better verb—and approached a taxi-driver who stared at him, and the fiddle, and slit his lips wide enough to demand:

"You gonna try to put that there thing in my cab?"

Douglas wiped the double perspiration of effort and embarrassment from his brow, and said "Yes" and someway managed to insert that fiddle in the cab. What's more, he made Olympia with both it, and himself, in one piece. But—

How long has it been since you've been to Olympia? That sportaceous edifice is equipped with glass doors that open with surprising reluctance for a place that encourages the paying customers to come in.

This Douglas discovered after he'd extracted that fiddle from the cab. Douglas got a door open, with one hand. With the other he was coyly embracing the fiddle. He tried to get the fiddle through. But he and the fiddle would not fit.

Douglas sought to push the fiddle ahead of him, but a bull fiddle is not a push-cart. Douglas just managed to keep the fiddle from being squashed by a closing door. Douglas said things. Well—

He might still be outside those swinging doors, if one of Olympia's alert staff hadn't noticed that something was amiss.

It took two attendants, a steam-fitter, a plumber, and Charlie Escoe (personally) to steer Douglas and fiddle into the building.

Douglas finally got the instrument to its owner, and was partly repaid by witnessing the almost tearfully joyous reunion betwixt the fiddle and the fiddler but—

Douglas shrugged off the thanks that were heaped upon him. And—

He did not hesitate to assure Jack Adams that he is going to try harder and harder to be a good hockey player—

Douglas thinks hockey is a nice, peaceful pastime, compared to a life-time of serfdom to a bull-headed bull fiddle. . . .

HER SPIRIT SHOWN ON

At just the time when the whole city of Cedar Falls, Iowa, was laying plans for the one-hundredth birthday of "Grandmother" Nancy Philpot, she fell and fractured her hip.

Consequently, the public celebration had to be called off, but on her birthday, she was quite perkily propped up in bed, in the room next to the living room, where her many friends dropped in to congratulate her.

Friends, and relatives, too, including three of her four grandsons living in Detroit: Frank, Harry, and Clem Jewell. Wayne, the fourth, could not get away.

Quite late on that birthday afternoon a belated guest hurried in, not really expecting to see "Grandmother" because she would be too weary after all the commotion. She noticed him, however, and motioned him into her room.

He bent over, kissed her forehead, and said:

"Aren't you tired after all this excitement, Grandmother?"

She smiled up at him, that matchless smile that has been so much a part of her personality for all these hundred years and answered:

"Yes, I am tired but—I'll have a long time to rest!"

IT'S HARDLY BEGUN

After all, there's nothing strange about the way in which a person can shuttle in and out of the life of another, particularly when they are as remote in age as a grown man and a pint-sized 12-year-old boy.

And that is the way it has been with Joe and Gary.

It was nearly a year ago that Joe sauntered over on a spring evening to watch his son, Bob, who's also around 12, play baseball on the corner lot.

Joe saw the group of youngsters, raising that pre-game commotion they almost always generate, and then his eyes fixed on the smallest lad in the group.

Not only was he smallest but his left arm was withered.

"Now, that's tough," thought Joe. "I suppose he's the umpire, or the water boy, or something."

It was about then that Bob noticed Joe and did something

rather unusual in son-and-father relationships. Instead of overlooking his dad, Bob actually sauntered out of that gesticulating group and came over to speak to him.

"Bob," said Joe, "who's that little kid with the bad left arm?"

"Oh," Bob answered, in a tone that seemed to settle everything, "that's Gary."

Joe was about to ask Bob "Well, who's Gary?" when a shout for Bob came up from that group, and away Bob dashed.

The game was about to begin, when Joe blinked his eyes. Small Gary, with a small glove on his left hand, marched to the pitcher's mound. And—

By the end of the first inning, Joe had decided that this Gary was about as neat a kid pitcher as ever he had seen—even better than he had been. (And most fathers will admit that, in their youth, they were remarkably good pitchers.)

So that was Joe's introduction to Gary.

Summer wiped its fevered brow, and autumn came to cool the earth, before, one evening, Bob came out of his dinner to say to his dad:

"Wish you'd been in our room in school today. Boy! We were all mixed up in arithmetic, and there was only one guy knew what it was all about. I honestly think he knew more than the teacher."

"Was that you?" Joe inquired, and Bob snorted:

"Me? I should say not. It was Gary."

"Oh?" said Joe. "The pitcher, eh?"

"Yeah," nodded Bob, "and the smartest kid in our grade and the class comedian, too!"

"Is he playing football?" Joe asked.

"Not this year," Bob said. "He's faster'n chain lightning but his folks think he's too small, yet. He's playin' tennis. He's the best tennis player in the whole school."

Autumn finally put on galoshes and became winter, and winter wore itself away until a couple of weeks ago.

Joe glanced down the street. He saw Bob, and a couple of lads who looked tall enough to be seniors in high school and, striding between that two—was Gary.

Bob detached himself from the group when it reached his door and came in.

"What have you been up to?" Joe asked and Bob answered: "Basketball game. Our team won."

"Does Gary play basketball?" Joe inquired and: "Sure," Bob nodded. "He's our center."

"Center?" Joe asked, "why he's not tall enough to play center!"

"He plays it against one of those big kids you just saw him with," Bob affirmed. "And of course, the big guy always beats him on the jump and tips the ball but that Gary's there to get it when it comes down."

"I am beginning to think," Joe said, "that this Gary is something."

"Beginning?" Bob said, "why everybody knows that Gary is just plain tops!"

"And in spite of that left arm," Joe was thoughtful.

"You know," Bob answered, "I don't really think Gary knows there's anything wrong with his left arm."

And then Bob shook his head, because Joe said one of those incomprehensible things that good fathers sometimes come out with, to the bewilderment of boys. Joe said:

"I have an idea that it isn't only Gary who's tops. I sort of think his parents are, too!"

GRANDMA QUERIES

The time has come in Grandma's life when her solicitous children are beginning to wonder if she isn't getting just a wee bit off the beam. Just to be on the safe side, her daughter, with whom she lives, got in touch with a psychologist, and made arrangements for him to drop over one afternoon and do a little sly checking on Grandma's mentality. He arrived, was introduced as a friend of Daughter's, and pretty soon he had lured Grandma into a side room.

There he pulled down the shades, so the general tone of the

place was dusky, and asked Grandma if she could catch her thumb.

Grandma complied neatly, and then the psychologist wondered if she could hold her left ear lobe with her right forefinger and thumb and, with her left forefinger, touch the tip of her nose.

After that was accomplished he tried a few other bits of mysterious mumbo-jumbo, thanked Grandma for her "cooperation" and went out, leaving her considerably in the dark as he murmured to Daughter: "I'll give you a report tomorrow."

Then he left the house, slamming the front door after him.

The echo of that slam hardly had subsided before a timorous Grandma came out of the darkened room and asked:

"Has that poor crazy man gone?"

BUMBLE AND GRANDMA'S HEN

My grandfather (said Bumble) was a long, lean man with a hunter's eye and a wide white mustache that waved when he was excited—which meant it waved most of the time—like a lace-curtain at an open window.

And that mustache went into a regular dipsy-do when my father bought me my first air-rifle. I guess I was six.

My grandfather was the one who taught me to aim it; to squeeze the trigger; to treat that air-gun with all the respect he himself had for the .30-.30 he just about adored.

Oddly enough, throughout all that training, Grandfather, who bellowed like a bull at the least excuse, was as gentle and patient as a mother guiding the steps of a little blind boy. Well—

One day I was out in the back yard behind the farmhouse, and Old Than, the hired man, said he didn't think I could hit my grandmother's pet hen, that was industriously scratching for scraps.

I don't think it even occurred to either Than or to me that if I did hit that hen, I'd hurt her.

And I guess I didn't really hurt her very much because—I hit her in the eye and she was dead, just like that—except for all the elaborate flopping and struggling which a hen goes through.

But I didn't stop to see the flopping. I went away from there as fast as my buckling knees could take me.

What I wanted right then was some place to hide; some nice dark cuddlesome spot away from a world gone suddenly horn mad.

The best place I could think of was 'way back under the huge double bed in the downstairs room off the kitchen, where Grandfather and Grandmother slept in winter when the upstairs was so hard to heat. So—

Into the consoling dusk I dived and tried not to hear Grandmother's outcries as she beheld her beloved Biddie doing her dance of death.

Then I heard Grandfather's voice. It boomed like surf on granite cliffs. It roared:

"Where's that cussed boy," and I could almost see the way in which his mustache was whipping up and down.

"Killin' a hen!" He went on. "I Crimus, I wish I was his father, so I could give him his lickin'. I Crimus, killin' a hen. Where is he?"

I lay there, quivering, beneath that bed, while the klump, klump, klump of Grandfather's cowhide boots grew louder. As did his voice:

"I know where that cussed boy is," he stated. "He's just where his father always went after he'd been up to some devilment. He's under a bed!"

Klump! Klump! Klump! of purposeful boots. Boots that came and stood like two misshapen pillars at the edge of my sanctuary.

"Boy," came that voice again, "you under that bed? You answer me!"

I couldn't have answered if I'd wanted to.

"No answer, huh? (I give you my word I could hear the words whistling through that embattled mustache.) "All right—do you come out from under that bed, or do I have to haul you out?"

A hand as big as a ham, at the end of an arm as big as a walking-beam joined the boots and began to grope under the bed. The voice thundered on:

"Don't you try to hide from me, Boy. You—Aha!" triumph there, because he'd caught me by an ankle.

He hauled me out into full view of the pitiless daylight.

I lay on my back with, oddly enough, that culprit air-rifle still clutched in my left fist. I stared up at that towering redwood of a man.

His mustache was working like mad; up and down and even twitching sideways. His hunter's eyes were blazing blue. His words were shots of dynamite:

"Gettin' so a man can't even feed the pigs in peace. Women yellin' so I could hear 'em 'way up at the barn. Killin' your grandmother's pet hen—

"Crimus!" and his voice went on to thunder-tones. "There's your grandma, out in the kitchen, cryin' her eyes out; and the hired girl havin' histericks all over the pantry. Jehu! I gotta mind to take a stick and give you a lickin' before your father gets home!"

Blue eyes that were augers twisting at my face; tones that were hammer-blows against my ears; a mustache that flapped like a Chinaman's shirt. And—just when I knew I couldn't stand it any longer; when the first, hot, unwanted tears lay at the corners of my eyes; that tamarack of a man bent down and down, and his voice went down and down, until it sifted, hardly more than a whisper, under that fluttering mustache, as he hissed:

"Did you hit that hen the first shot?"

FATHER'S PHILOSOPHY

The other evening we listened as the father of two smallish boys discussed with the father of two smallish girls the relative advantages of boys or girls in a family.

Finally, the father of the boys came out with this one:

"The only advantage I can see to having girls is that it doesn't matter much how badly you spoil them as you bring them up, because some other man will keep right on with the spoiling where you left off."

SHADOW AND SUBSTANCE

When Anna grew old enough to ask the prim Aunt Mildred with whom she lived, where her parents were, Aunt Mildred said that they had died when Anna was very young.

"Sometime," she promised, "I will tell you about it." And that was enough for Anna, at that time. But, as the years began their upward climb she wanted to know more.

"Your father," said Aunt Mildred, "died in a, er, a railroad accident. Your mother died right afterward, of a broken heart, I think."

She seemed loath to say anything else. It was not until Anna's curiosity had become, as it should become with the growing, an impelling thing, that, one day, her Aunt said, impatiently:

"You're 12 years old, and if you insist on knowing how your father died, I guess you're old enough.

"You have," she went on, "two brothers and a sister. But when your parents passed on, well, your relatives divided you children among them, to bring you up. Your father," she added, "was very poor. But then, he had been ill so long. . . ."

Aunt Mildred hesitated, and said: "Of course, you realize that I am not your real aunt. I am the widow of your mother's brother, and so I do not know all the facts. Your uncle never said much. But—

"Your father was killed by a train on the Santa Fe tracks at Colorado Springs. He had gone there to steal loose pieces of coal.

"Oh," she granted, "I guess he had to steal because you see, he had been ill for a long time. He and your mother and you children moved to Colorado Springs for his health. And then—

"All four of you children had typhoid fever, and he did not have a job, and it was winter, and, well, I guess he just had to take that coal."

So there was the blunt story at last, and, in the tones in which Aunt Mildred spoke, were the overtones of shame—

A shame that somehow imparted itself to the growing Anna;

an Anna who grew to dream of a pale, scrawny man, killed while stealing coal from the railroad tracks. But—

Such is the protective trait of humans that when Anna was in high school and one of her teen-age girl-friends asked her about her father, Anna said:

"My daddy was killed when I was just a little girl. It was really tragic. He was taking a short cut to our home in Colorado Springs, and that meant he had to cross the Santa Fe tracks.

"He saw some poor children picking up coal—and a train was coming.

"There was no time for a warning, so he just ran and managed to throw the last of those children off the tracks before the train got there but, he couldn't jump clear. He was killed."

Anna's girl-friend began retelling that story, and, in no time at all, Anna shone in the glory of her father's heroic death. And—

As the years went on, the time came when she nearly believed it herself. It was so much easier. And such a completely human thing to do.

As human as it was, last fall, when she was in Denver, to go to Colorado Springs and, being there, to start wondering about where she had lived as a baby.

She sought out the records. She found the very street, the very house—a sadly shabby little house that looked to her, as she stood in front of it, far too small for a scrawny man, and his wife, and four children. . . .

An elderly woman stepped out on the porch of the place next door. And Anna heard herself asking:

"I wonder if you ever heard of a family named Sheridan living in that house?"

The woman replied: "Yes. Of course I remember the Sheridans."

"I'm the youngest daughter," Anna said.

The woman studied her. She smiled. "You look a little like that fine man, your father." She hesitated. She asked: "I suppose you know how he was killed?"

Anna straightened her shoulders, in the presence at last, not of her dream, but the reality. She said: "Yes, I know."

The woman said: "I have always thought there was some reason we will never understand why it was that he came along at just the right moment to push those children off the tracks."

WITH A CANE

We are not sure we are right in printing the following; and yet, well, here it is, from a man whose every word we have every reason to believe:

"The other afternoon," he said, "I stood on Woodward Avenue, downtown, waiting for my wife and leaning on the cane without which I cannot get around—as I have not been able to be cane-free for years. And then—

"I saw one coming: a Trouble-maker—

"A man with a cane gets to know those Trouble-makers, and this one telegraphed his intention, as they almost always do.

"He paused in his stride, looked me over (and there is little enough of me to look over), looked at my cane. Then—

"He came on toward me and, just as he reached me, he gave a vicious swing of his hip.

"That was intended to knock me sprawling, and it would have knocked me sprawling except that I, out of my years of experience, swerved out of his way, and he staggered past me, regained his balance, and went on, never once looking back. You see:

"The Trouble-maker is one of the hazards a man, particularly a small man, who has to rely on a cane, comes to expect. As I learned a good many years ago, when I was working with criminals in the Big House at Waupun, Wisconsin.

"Two or three of those Trouble-makers tried, in some vague way, to explain their actions.

"As far as I could put their thoughts together, they like to vent their wrath on society in general by 'accidentally' knocking down someone, especially the physically handicapped. And here is the strange thing:

"Having done that, they are the first to offer sympathy and assistance."

Here the man speaking paused, lighted a cigaret, and went on:

"Also, one of those Trouble-makers wised me up on how to avoid getting knocked down on the street.

"First, of course, you have to be able to recognize Trouble when it is on its way. Then, as he passes you, he draws back his shoulder to swing it hard, and send you flying. But—

"If you swing your shoulder just as he is drawing his back, Trouble takes a fall.

"One day on Woodward I saw Trouble approaching:

"With a careful overlooking of my presence, he drew his shoulder back. So I hit him with mine. . . .

"As he picked himself up, he looked me over speculatively and asked:

" 'What Big House you from?'

" 'Waupun,' I said, and he growled:

" 'I shoulda known it!' and slouched away."

CAUSE AND EFFECT

Zel says there may not be any connection but that he knows a young man whose engagement was announced Friday night.

Saturday morning he went into a barber shop, sat in the chair, and told the barber:

"Give me a haircut!"

The barber goggled, "Like thaaat?" in some astonishment, because the young man had sat down in the chair wearing his overcoat and hat. . . .

LOCALITY

Yesterday we heard about an incident in the trial of a woman accused of maltreating her small son.

On the witness stand was a woman brought there by the defense to show that the mother was neither malicious nor mean. Her attorney asked:

"Madam, did you ever see the defendant strike the child?"

The witness smiled and answered:

"Why, yes. I saw her give him a light spanking, once."

"And where was that?" asked the attorney, trying, as lawyers will and should, to have the place of the happening in the record of the trial.

But the witness had a different answer. She said:

"Right on the spot the Lord intended children to be spanked."

At that moment the Judge snorted:

"Madam, what was that you said?"

The witness bridled, and simpered: "Oh, you know where I mean!" and the judge responded:

"Madam, it is not the anatomy I am questioning, but the theology."

SO LIFELIKE!

Joe Mitchell phoned in to say that in his opinion, these plastic mannequins of the simulated feminine persuasion that stand in store windows, modeling dresses, are getting altogether too doggone human.

Yesterday, he saw one with a run in her stocking.

CONCENTRATION

Fathers who tear their thinning hair about the way in which today's teen-agers seem to like to study their lessons with the radio blaring at them, may get some comfort out of the following actuality:

Joe, dad to Suzanne, who is a senior in high school, and who has been on the honor list since she was in the ninth grade, grew a bit impatient the other evening.

Three times in 15 minutes, he tried to use the downstairs phone, only to find that Suzanne was occupying the upstairs extension.

At the end of 20 minutes, Joe, heartless man that he is, clumped upstairs to tell Suzanne it was time for her to lay off the lingo and give him a chance.

And it does show how heartless Joe is, to want to stop a conversation of merely 20 minutes! What Miss Seventeen doesn't plan on at least half an hour's chit-chat?

Especially when, at the other end of the line, is someone as charming as Bill, another high school senior and, mark you, a youth who also has been on the honor list since the ninth grade.

Joe, however, stopped in the doorway and stared at Suzanne:

She had the portable radio in the room, going medium-volume.

She had the phone receiver set to her ear between her left shoulder and neck.

She was lying flat on her stomach on the floor.

With her right hand she was busy with a pencil and a pad of paper, making references to the mathematics book propped in front of her.

"Shucks," thought Joe, remorsefully, "I guess she and Bill are doing their lessons."

But a few moments' of her conversation didn't sound that way. So Joe set his jaw, walking around where she could see him, the heartless wretch grimly drew his finger across his throat in the radio signal that means "Cut."

Suzanne said wearily: "Well, Bill, I guess the Old Man wants to use the phone. I'll call you back later." Then she cradled the receiver.

Joe asked: "Were you two swapping lessons? It didn't sound that way to me."

And here's what Suzanne, honor student, and product of the radio age, replied:

"Oh, we were studying, and visiting. I was doing my math and Bill was doing his French. But we weren't just idly chatting.

"He had his radio tuned to a different program from the one I was listening to, so he was telling me the gags that were coming in on his program, and I was telling him the jokes that were coming in on mine."

ANTI-ORANGE BLOSSOM

Beverly Bertrand is going around with this one: "Have you heard about the girl who lost her boy-friend by making too many parsonal remarks?"

HE GOT MISPLACED

The jolly social evenings of an undertakers' association in one part of the city have settled back to cheerful, beer-drinking evenings, now that Sammy, the smarty-pants, has departed.

Even Sammy's ex-boss doesn't miss him much, and savors the way in which he vanished from that amiable group who, for months, have been in the habit of gathering about every two weeks in one of the funeral homes.

During these social evenings, the undertakers escape the strain of their profession by drinking beer, eating bread and cheese, playing poker or cribbage, or by just sitting around and chewing the fat.

While no particular taboo has been laid down about conversational topics they tacitly steer clear of discussing what happens after rigor mortis becomes rigorous.

And since these gentlemen are both genial and gregarious, they willingly agreed when Sammy's boss asked if he could bring Sammy, his new assistant, to the next soiree.

Sammy was not a success as a guest. He turned out to be a brash and opinionated young man who butted in and flattened out any statement made by his elders.

By the end of the evening, everyone was fed up with Sammy, the Smarty-Pants, and it was silently agreed that he wouldn't be invited again. But—

The undertakers didn't know much about human nature, if they thought Sammys of this world are going to be left out in the cold.

Sammy somehow learned when the next session was to be held, and he was on hand.

Also, he was at his obnoxious best, implying by tone and gesture that he was a high peak of intelligence sprouting out of a whole flock of round-domed foot-hills.

Sammy had mangled two more gatherings before one member whom we'll call O'Malley, a long, lean, lugubrious citizen with a charming mortuary manner, phoned Sammy's boss and said:

"Look, Joe. That assistant of yours is a pain in the neck and you know it. Us guys have been thinking up a little scheme that might tame him down the next time he crashes a meeting. Will that be okay with you?"

Joe said it certainly would and how could he help.

"Just bring him to a meeting a week from tonight in the back room of my shop," said O'Malley, and added, darkly: "By the way, don't look around for me. I'll be there. But you may not see me."

When Sammy and his boss entered O'Malley's back room, the lights there seemed doubly dim, and the chairs were set up near a rough box, with its lid down.

"O'Malley'll be here in a little while," observed a gent named Mortimer. "He had a hurry call. Morgue. Let's visit, because I've sure had a strange experience."

With that, Mortimer began to tell about something spooky that had happened to him that day.

Hardly had Mortimer gotten under way than Sammy cut in with:

"Blaah! There's no such thing as spooks."

He plunged into his own opinions and he'd gone along for quite a while when abruptly he stopped, cocked an ear at that rough box, and asked: "Say! Did I hear a noise in that box?"

Those present stared at each other, and shook their heads. Mortimer said:

"You couldn't have. The gangster in there is so full of holes he's permanently defunct."

Sammy started expounding again. But again he stopped abruptly, to snap: "I tell you, I did hear a noise in that box."

"You couldn't have," Mortimer insisted.

"I'm going to sssseee," said Sammy and walked to the box.

Just as he reached it, the lid lifted a little and out slid a long, lean, bare, bony arm and a dead-white hand. The hand clamped around Sammy's wrist.

Sammy squeaked like a creaky hinge and went out of there like a bat out of a bazooka. And—he hasn't been seen in undertaking circles since.

His departure allowed O'Malley to emerge from the rough box, casually clamping an empty beer bottle between his left arm and his ribs.

He was rubbing his hands, not gleefully, but rather as might a man whose hands are just about frozen. And, as a matter of fact, they were, because:

To lend the last fine touch to his scheme, O'Malley had been holding his hands on a cake of ice in the rough box, the better to give Sammy, the Smarty-Pants, the Icy Paw. . . .

NON-COOPERATION

Through the eyes of Al Ash, Jr., we suspect we know what, if anything, is the matter with the Detroit Police Department—internal friction.

Al was glancing out his downtown window the other day and saw an empty automobile parked contentedly in a "No Parking" zone.

Just then, along the street klip-klopped a mounted policeman on his well-polished steed.

The officer spotted that car, swung from the saddle, looped the bridle reins over his arm and, digging deep in his pocket, came out with a violations pad and pencil.

He braced one foot on the rear bumper and started to write out a ticket.

Whereupon, Mr. Horse r'ared back on the bridle, yanking the reins and pulling the officer off balance.

The policeman gave the horse a glare and a haul at the reins, dragged him back into docility, and again started to write that ticket.

Mr. Horse snuck up behind his partner, snaked a neck around his shoulder and, for gosh sakes, in nimble teeth, he grabbed that pad right out of his master's hands.

And the officer had a heck of a time getting the pad back!

SO CONSOLING

On-the-ball, Paul Aird said:

"I am reminded of the doctor who attended my invalid mother. I think he was as much a psychologist as a physician."

Mother had fretted for months about her heart. It thumped, it bumped, it creaked, it squeaked, it limped, "and I'm sure it will be the death of me," she frequently complained to Paul when he dropped over to see her. And then, one fine day:

She was all brightness and delight when Paul came in.

"Why so cheerful?" Paul asked.

"The doctor was here just now," she answered, "and he gave my heart a good examination and he says it's in fine shape."

Knowing what he did about his mother's condition, Paul was thinking to himself that the doctor certainly had been painting an optimistic picture, when his mother added:

"He told me that my heart will last just as long as I do."

A CHILD'S EYE VIEW

He couldn't have been a day more than four years old. He had on an absurdly mannish little coat, and a pair of straight pants about the length of a postage stamp.

He came out of the main room where they'd been holding Sunday School. His eyes were as large as dollars, and black with fright.

He stopped in the hall, stared around, stared up at us, spun on a small heel and started back into the big and by-now empty room.

"What's the matter, Sonny?" we asked.

He stopped and peered back over his shoulder. His mouth was screwed down at the corners, pinched tight, as if he were holding in a sob. And suddenly we understood:

He was lost.

Again he started into that big room, toward the smaller rooms at the back. He began to run.

He probably thought he was going like a buzzing bullet. We went after him at a clumsy trot. We called, consolingly:

"Don't worry, Sonny, we'll find your mother."

He ran faster, all alone there in that room that must have seemed as big to him as Briggs Stadium. That big a place and being followed by a strange mis-shapen monster with a voice like a fog-horn.

He spurted through the back door of that room, along a corridor.

At its far end, a Sunday school teacher appeared. She called:

"Where have you been, Johnny? Your mother's back here, looking for you."

Although he went into a real spurt of speed, we were able to see the end of his rush:

The flying tackle he put on his mother's knees, and the way he buried his face in her skirt. . . .

As we turned away, we remembered all too well one of the most ghastly experiences we ever have had—

An experience we imagine is part of the growing up process of almost every grown-up—

The experience of getting lost, as we were lost in the Jordan, Marsh store in Boston.

(And since that time we have been convinced that every child should have, sewed into his clothes, his name and address, because we were so frightened we simply could not speak.)

We suppose we were not misplaced for more than 15 minutes, but during that time, we lived a long lost generation. And the things we saw!

Those "mis-shapen monsters" we mentioned a few moments ago.

Because—

Even the most beautiful person in the world, a mother, is misshapen in appearance to a smallish child.

It is, of course, merely a matter of foreshortening that brings the adult jaw out into a jut as prognathous as the jaw of an ape; that makes a group of kindly grown-ups, standing around a small lost child, looking down, seem like some horrible group of giants and ogres right out of "Jack and the Bean Stalk"—

Come to think of it, probably the prime origin of ogres and their ilk grew out of the memories men carried into manhood of the way that adults looked to them when they were very young.

Yes, the Child's Eye View of the world must be pretty distressing.

Consider the case of the youngster, clutching his mother's hand, pattering along a crowded downtown sidewalk, surrounded by tree trunks that move, and—

'Way up there in the clouds, with their tremendous jowls and beaked noses, those strange beings among whom a child has to dwell and, with whom he some how has to cope.

Think of the kindergartner, on his first day in school! How high the ceilings, and how great the building!

Think of the dizzying distance from top to bottom of a flight of simple stairs!

Think of a small one squeezed into an elevator!

Think, come to think of it, of a kid-let in a movie!

No wonder he breathes down the back of your neck, as he tries to see the screen, when, between the screen and him, are two or more odd-shaped mountains, that are the heads and shoulders of the grown-ups ahead.

And small wonder that to the small boy, his father is the biggest man in all the world.

Perhaps we take too much space on this subject, but the more we think about it, the more we realize it must take an uncommon amount of courage and of faith, not to mention confusion and no small amount of fear, for those who have the Child's Eye View—

Those plucky little persons, two feet high, who struggle in a world designed for five feet ten. . . .

HE'LL GET ALONG

Eric the Badger avers that youthful Miss Deedee lives in Milwaukee in the 10000 block North and the 4000 block West.

She has a boy-friend named Vern, who dwells in the 12000 block South and the 3000 block East.

In view of these distances, when they recently decided to go to a high school basketball game, they agreed to meet in front of the Airlines Building, which is just midway.

Miss Deedee arrived promptly on the moment but—Vern was nowhere to be seen. And the minutes began to tick. And then:

Inside the Airlines Building the telephone at the Information desk went dingle!

The clerk answered it, to hear a youthful masculine voice plead:

"Lady, will you please look around and pick out a pleasant-faced man and call him to the phone?"

"Whaaat?" demanded the clerk.

"A pleasant-faced man, please," urged the voice. "I've got an important message for him."

The information clerk shook her head sadly, partly at this request, partly at the zaniness of the world in general, and took a look at the customers.

Quite near at hand was a well-fed citizen smoking a cigar with placid, pleasant puffs.

"Mister," she called, "you're wanted on the phone."

The man pulled the cigar from his mouth. "Me?" he asked. "Nobody I know, knows I'm in Milwaukee."

"You're wanted," the clerk was emphatic. "You have a very pleasant face."

Maybe he had a pleasant face but it was pretty puzzled as he took the phone and said: "Hello?"

Promptly came that youthful voice.

And there was real urgency in that youthful voice as it said:

"Listen, Mister, I'm in a jam with my girl-friend and I need your help!

"I had to work overtime and I didn't get a chance to phone her and she's expecting me to meet her outside the main door of that Airlines Building, as of 10 minutes ago.

"So, Mister, will you just step outside and tell her, please, that I'll meet her at the gym where there's gonna be that basketball game. I—"

"Wait a minute," from Pleasant-Face. "How'm I going to know her? Is she—"

"Mister," came the answer from Vern, "I was just going to tell you. She's very pretty, and she will be standing there tapping the sidewalk with her right foot, and there will be sparks in her eyes.

"You'll recognize her all right," Vern reassured, "because she sure is a pretty girl, especially when she is mad, like she is mad right now. And, Mister, you might smooth things over a little if you told her you recognized her because she was such a pretty girl.

"And one thing more, Mister: maybe you better not tell her what I said about tapping the pavement, and sparks in her eyes, and her being mad. You know how women are."

"I do, Son, I do," said Pleasant-Face, and to the tune of Vern's "Thank you," Pleasant-Face cradled the phone, and delivered the message.

THE SECOND SILENCE

Mr. and Mrs. Martin have been married long enough now to have gone into the Second Silence and—they don't like it very well.

In the days of the First Silence, when they were bride and groom, they were so busy patterning their lives, fitting them together, that they didn't realize it was a Silence.

But the time came when, sometimes, and particularly on a rainy Sunday afternoon, each of them, secretly, looked yearningly back on the peaceful hours of the First Silence.

Now it has come again, after 25 years, because their youngest child has grown so old that he has followed their other children out of the Martin home, to live his own life.

And so Mr. and Mrs. Martin have come to the Second Silence; just the two of them again, dwelling in an echoing house that seems, some way, resentful at the absence of hurried little feet; and family arguments; and the generally rambunctious presence of youth. . . .

VERY HUSH-HUSH

Young Pete's mother made a surprise visit to his school room recently, and was surprised to find him being punished by having to sit on the floor in front of the whole class.

When Pete came home from school, Mother told him how much his behavior had hurt her, "And," she added, "your father is going to be just awfully shocked."

Promptly, Pete, with some dread of the wood-shed where his father might express his sentiments, pleaded with Mother not to tell him.

Finally, Mother agreed that it would be their secret.

The next afternoon, Pete came running home from school and burst in the front door with:

"Mother—you and I have got another secret!"

NOT ALONE

In certain circles in Ann Arbor they still speak of an incident during the recent J-Hop.

As the Sophomore reported it to us:

"There was gay conversation and some friendly pushing as the young couples edged slowly up a long staircase to the ballroom for the great college J-Hop.

"Crisp black tuxedos, colorful evening gowns, eager faces—all were blended into a moving sea of anticipation . . .

"The press of people around him only made him glad, or so his smile said:

"His face glowed, and mirrored the excitement in his brain.

"The girl beside him must have understood, for she seemed happy too. In fact, her smile was so warm and dazzling that scarcely anyone noticed the tight grip her fingers kept on his left elbow.

"At the top of the stairs, the crowd moved on, but he stopped and she waited patiently beside him.

"His lips quivered for a moment and he grasped her hand.

"She watched him through misty eyes until, at last, he nodded, and then, with chin held high, she guided her blind young man through the archway and into the most unforgettable of all college dances."

QUITE A WOMAN!

In spite of the telephone silences that yawned in this office Monday, Betty Ransom called in to report "one of the most horrid sights I've ever seen!"

Last Thursday, Betty was one of a line of persons waiting in a smallish suburban post office to send out money orders. Just in front of Betty was a quiet-looking little lady, neatly put together and wearing that lift of chin that betokens so often the grim determination of small women.

Suddenly, somewhere back in the line, was a scream. And—

"There's a mouse in here," cried another woman.

Betty felt an overpowering temptation to climb up on a chair, only there wasn't a chair. But that little woman ahead of her!

She sprang out of line demanding, "Where's that mouse?" saw it cowering in one corner of the room, descended upon it with cat-like steps and, with incredible dexterity, caught that struggling mouse by the tail.

Holding it violently a-dangle in one hand, she managed, with the other, to get her big hand-bag open.

Into the handbag she popped that mouse, zipped the bag shut, walked easily to her place in line—it certainly was waiting for her—and remarked, contentedly over her shoulder to Betty:

"I'll just take it home to my cat for an Easter Sunday dinner."

CROOKED?

Joe Clark, the top-flight photographer who's recently been converted to wearing a hat, which has nothing to do with this item, only it shows that wifely pressure, diligently applied, can finally make a man hat-conscious, went to the D&K Camera Repair Shop recently.

He was chatting with one of the veterans who run that establishment when there came solid-sounding steps outside the door, and in klumped one of the city's policemen lugging, of all things, one of those nickel candy-vending machines.

"Can you fix this thing?" the Officer demanded.

The veteran said it didn't look much like a camera to him, but he could try.

The Officer, with the delicate perceptivity of his profession, sensed a bit of curiosity, so he explained:

"This machine is located in our precinct station. The proceeds go to our Boy Scout troop. Well, the darn thing won't work—some Copper put a slug in it."

BUDGETED

The self-same Bostonian who conceded Frank Sinatra had done pretty well for a person born, not in Boston, but in Hoboken, N. J., has definite ideas on the subject of the household budget.

Wary Mary and her husband, this Bostonian and his wife, got to talking about that ticklish subject, and the Bostonian observed:

"My wife and I have no budgetary troubles. We always end the year with a surplus."

Wary Mary sort of hoped her husband hadn't heard that statement because in their family the budget takes a beating. . . .

It was somewhat later the same evening that Wary Mary found herself getting more confidential with the Bostonian's wife—at that time he was across the room with some of the men and making some mention of Harvard, which is a university.

The Bostonian's wife sort of giggled in a slightly Sullivan Square manner and said:

"You know, I had some trouble keeping my face straight when my husband said we live within our budget."

"Oh," breathed Wary Mary.

"It actually is a fact," the wife went on, "that we do. But that is because each of the last five years some aunt or other has died and left us from one to five thousand dollars."

Here she paused and fetched a sigh, adding:

"What's bothering us right now is that we are rapidly running out of aunts."

SOMETHING TO BARK ABOUT

We feel we are safe in announcing that Thel Burgert has really bought himself a bird dog. The basis of this statement is what happened the other day when this dog, "Freckles" by name, and a mere five-months-old setter, managed to worm his way through the picket fence that marches sedately around the Burgert manse, and went high-tailing it down the street.

Thel looked after him, at a distance of about a block, yelping for Freckles to come home. Then—

Suddenly, Freckles disappeared, right off the face of the earth. But only for a short time. He abruptly reappeared through the front door of a house, followed by a woman who was doing her neighborly best not to be too irate.

And what do you think had happened?

With an intuition the far side of uncanny, that baby bird-dog had charged into a house that contained a canary. In his clumsy puppyish way he'd tried to point the canary, but had managed to knock over the cage. Whereupon the bird flew the coop.

What boots it, though, to Thel, that the replacement value of the canary was $6 plus state tax. Think of a bird dog so astute it can, in a crowded city, ferret out even a canary!

HIS THANKS

The district in which Mrs. Jones lives was properly excited when back from the war came Roy, veteran of three years overseas—

He was in the North African invasion, in Sicily, in Italy, in Southern France, and finally, when the bullets stopped snapping, in Germany.

He's as normally untalkative as most of those men are, until someone gets them wound up. But he can register bewilderment all right, and he did—Monday.

To call on him came young Jim, who was drafted last September and since has been at the Aberdeen proving grounds. Jim looked Roy over, seeing, through his hurriedly purchased civilian clothes, the row of ribbons that always will march across Roy's left breast. Then—

Jim, the rookie, stuck out his hand and said to Roy:

"I want you to know that we civilians certainly appreciate what you soldiers did for us."

HE UNSTUCK THE CELLAR DOOR

Elmore Frank, meter reader for the Edison Company, had no way of knowing he was walking into a dilemma as he strolled past a bowling alley and into the tavern next door.

He eased his way through the characters with which that place was filled, and down to the basement for his appointment with the meter.

The task accomplished, he naturally expected to go on to more readings but—the basement door said no! It had developed a mean temper and refused to budge.

Since this sometimes happens in Frank's line of business, it caused him small concern, because he has discovered that a little noise usually will bring someone down to see what and who's cooking. However:

Although Frank went into Phase One of getting out, which is loud shouting, and into Phase Two, which is banging on the water pipes, nothing happened.

Not only were the beer-drinkers upstairs engaged in loud if sudsy arguments, but the jukebox was giving out, and, like distant thunder came the bang and thud of balls and pins from the next-door bowling alley. So:

How was Frank to get out?

In a resourceful sort of way, he tapped the problem right at its source:

He noticed a valve in the pipe that wafted beer from the downstairs kegs to the bar above. He pensively turned off that tap. He was liberated—and quick.

LITTLE ROCHELLE

Little Rochelle is a sweet little miss of only a few summers, whose life is a series of uninhibited, adult-startling questions.

Recently, her mother was entertaining mixed company and the conversation veered over to the subject of the maternity ward of the nearest hospital.

Came a pause in the discussion and Little Rochelle leaned far forward, her mouth opening.

Mother quivered. But—Rochelle paused reflectively, and the lull disappeared, and Little Rochelle leaned back in her chair.

Came another pause and again Little Rochelle leaned forward. And again Mother braced herself for what might happen. But once more Little Rochelle merely closed her lips, and Mother subsided, practically mopping her brow.

The third time a pause came, however, Rochelle speared her mother with an eager eye and demanded: "Mother, why are you holding your breath?"

LITTLE PITCHERS

The eternal feminine! At what age does it become beauty-conscious? In the cradle? The nursery? The—well anyhow:

Aub Reebel had no more than entered his home Friday evening than Joey, the six-year-old son, somewhat towing Janet, his four-year-old sister, assailed Reebel with a strictly sensible question.

"Daddy," said Joey, "the radio says there's going to be a cold wave. What's that?"

Reebel went into a good fatherly explanation and, ignoring a faint frown on the fair brow of Janet, ended up with:

"Now, Joey, do you know what a cold wave is?"

"Yes, Daddy," nodded Joey.

"I thought," observed four-year-old Janet, "I thought it was a permanent."

ANYTHING COULD HAPPEN

James D. Cole, 5783 Vermont, starts right out by saying:

"Six weeks ago, a bit of a cat called 'Tiger' decided to adopt my family, as well as the neighbors, and so we became the somewhat reluctant owners of half-a-cat; meaning, he spends the morning and up to late afternoon with us, and the remainder of the 24 hours with our neighbors.

"A few weeks back I began to notice that Tiger seemed to catch a mouse every morning.

"Being unemployed, and consequently feeling the time heavy on my hands, I became even more observant—I noticed that these mice that dangled from Tiger's mouth as he stalked proudly across the neighbor's yard, morning after morning, seemed identical in size.

"On each occasion, Tiger toted that mouse to the shelter of our second-growth lilacs, and one morning I decided to see what happened next. . . .

"Secure within our fenced-in yard, Tiger laid his prize on the ground and proceeded to play the ancient game of Cat-and-Mouse with him for about half an hour. And then—

"Tiger turned his back upon that mouse, tucked his forepaws beneath his chest, and went to sleep. And the mouse rambled under our porch to safety."

Feeling this was a strange state of affairs, Cole settled himself on the back porch, puffing his pipe and reflecting on the laziness of city cats in general and then:

"I nearly fell off the porch because that mouse came out from under it, and scampered right up to the dozing cat and proceeded to sniff noses with him.

"At which, Tiger, dreamily opened one eye, reached out a paw, cuffed the mouse, and went back to sleep.

"Realization came to me in a flash—all those many mice Tiger had caught boiled down to one mouse—a playmate!

"To verify my theory, I've been starting my vigil earlier in the mornings and here's what happens:

"Tiger comes to our porch and miaows. Out comes the mouse. Tiger picks him up in his jaws and races madly down the middle of the block, only to stalk back slowly. After this triumphant march, they get behind those lilac bushes and have their morning frolic. . . ."

LIONS PHOOEY!

John had his nose pretty deep in the paper the other day as he sat at his favorite lunch table.

He was reading that story about six, or was it seven, lions that got loose, only they didn't, thereby frightening the community no end.

Abruptly, John realized someone was leaning over his shoulder.

It turned out to be his personable waitress.

She, with a habit doubtless picked up in street cars, was reading his paper.

"What you reading?" quizzed John placidly.

"That story about the lions," observed the waitress, and added "Lions, phooey!"

Noticing that John's eyebrows climbed upstairs, she explained: "I don't see why folks should be worried about seven lions let loose, when there are at least six wolves to every block."

GREAT DIFFERENCE

"Horses" has come cantering back from Miami bringing with him what he insists is an accurate report of what happened when the cook in a family he knows there, flew the coop.

Forthwith the mistress of that home advertised for a suitable successor and in the course of time came a well-padded citizeness who really looked promising.

Came the customary amount of sparring between mistress and prospect, dealing with references, and pay and days off, and all those things.

And these were eventually so smoothed out that both parties began to look contented and prepared to try it out.

At that point, however, the cook suddenly said:

"Oh, they's one other thing I gotta ask."

"What's that?" asked the mistress. And the cook came back:

"About yo' vegetables. Does yo' Birdseye or does yo' peel?"

WHY THE BIRDS SOUND PEEVISH

We cannot understand why it is that we have "it" for mourning doves. All the mourning doves on Grosse Ile come and camp under our open window each pre-dawn and there emit their mournful moo. Now—

We don't want anyone to think we are allergic to our feathered friends. We get along amiably with wrens, robins, sparrows, orioles, horned owls, and bald headed eagles. But mourning doves!

It is our studied opinion the sound they exhale should be reserved exclusively for the back room of a cow-barn.

We're convinced that mourning doves are the alarm clock of the bird-world. We believe that all our other birdies would sleep at least another hour in the morning, if those dingbusted mourning doves didn't wake 'em up.

And to our conviction we add solidity by a fact you may have noticed:

In the diapason of bird-song that rises to greet the oncoming sun, you may have noticed many an angry overtone. That is only natural. The birds are sore at being awakened prematurely by those mourning doves. . . .

IT DEPENDS

Jim was present when a native-born American reporter interviewed one of the more recent British brides to reach these shores.

After the customary sparring around, in which the reporter was trying to dig up something new in a field that's been pretty thoroughly investigated, he took another tack and said:

"Living in America, do you think you'll lose your accent?"

The bride looked startled, and queried:

"Have I an accent?"

The reporter grinningly answered: "You certainly have."

"How odd," the bride exclaimed. "I was just thinking what a strange accent you have."

Both stared at each other a moment before the bride observed:

"I guess an accent rawther depends on who is where."

GEORGIA PEACH

Among those here for the Golden Jubilee, was Ty Cobb who, in his own field, did much to advertise Detroit the length and breadth of this land.

It was our pleasure to have seen Cobb many a time out at Bennett Park—In fact, we sometimes wonder at our energy. We would forsake Old Central High School (Wayne University) and walk to Bennett Park, and then stand up to watch the game.

But what we had in mind was the trick a group of roving sports writers played on the fiery Georgian during an exhibition trip that followed spring training one season when Cobb was at his peak.

In each city where an exhibition was to be played there naturally was a brass band at the ball park. And this is what those writers did:

One of their members, with a strictly sober face, would approach the bandmaster and say:

"Look, you'd like to do something to please Ty Cobb, wouldn't you?"

To which the bandmaster naturally would agree, so the writer would go on with: "Well, when Cobb comes to bat, there's a tune he loves above all others. Play it for him, won't you?"

The upshot was that Cobb was practically raving at a Yankee conspiracy by the time the tour was over. The tune was "Marching Through Georgia."

SHE WINS

Two or three weeks after we'd printed a weird list of names compiled by Robert L. Matthews, III, we received a letter from Mrs. H. R. Williamson, 9108 Cameron street, saying:

"I am sure I know a name that tops the name of any person in Detroit.

"This is my aunt's name. When I was a little girl, grandmother would tell it to me, and finally I decided to write it for safe keeping. Her full name is:

"Liza Mae Jane Lucas Ben Dixon Pyano Come Eyther Go Yonder Mare Marina Madina Susan Aitch Thundergust Huldagust Stalldeep and Spanish Oh Moore!

"We call her," added Mrs. Williamson, " 'Hun' for short."

Having quirked a quizzical eyebrow at that name we instanter wrote Mrs. Williamson asking quite a few questions about that aunt, the existence of whom, except in the beautiful realms of imagination, we doubted. Yesterday we had this reply:

"No wonder you want more information about such a name. Well:

"Aunt Hun lives with me at 9108 Cameron street. She was born Dec. 25, 1867, and is now 78 years of age.

"As to how she came to get the name of 'Liza Mae Jane Lucas Ben Dixon Pyano Come Eyther Go Yonder Mare Marina Madina Susan Aitch Thundergust Huldagust Stalldeep and Spanish Oh Moore'—

"She says that an old friend of the family wanted to name her, so Grandmother just added on the names the friend wanted to those she had already given her.

"Aunt Hun didn't grow very tall (less than five feet) which she says is directly due to having so much name to carry. Hope this doesn't sound too unbelievable because it is really true."—Mrs. H. R. Williamson.

THEY ALSO SERVE

In these days when the philosophy of "Put-me-first" is so appallingly predominant, it might be nice to think about Don and Janet and Anne.

Don and Janet have been undergoing the restrictions of caring for a wee son. And then came the chance for a carefree week-end away from home.

Industriously, they rounded up a nurse to stay with the infant. She was to come Friday noon and stay until the following Monday morning.

Thursday afternoon, the nurse's daughter telephoned saying her mother had been taken ill and couldn't possibly come for the week-end.

Now—a week-end may not seem like long to some, but to a pair of new parents, it can be a great deal of time indeed; something distressing to forego. So Don and Janet began frantically phoning to see if they couldn't find a substitute.

Naturally, they turned to Anne, a kindly matron in the neighborhood who somehow manages, unobtrusively, to be a part of the lives of so many different persons.

Don told Anne his troubles—could she recommend a nurse?

Anne made a few suggestions but Don called gloomily back Thursday night saying none of them had panned out. "And so," he sighed, "I guess our week-end trip is off."

"Oh, no," said Anne, cheerily, "I should say not. I'll take care of the baby myself." . . . And she did.

AS REQUESTED:

Charlotte and Paul were doing a spot of home-painting. Charlotte was upstairs; Paul, down.

Things went along in a pleasant conjugal silence for a while, then Paul heard a sloshy sort of thump upstairs, and he knew perfectly well what had happened:

Charlotte, in her zeal, had managed to kick over the pail of paint.

In a few moments her whimsical voice floated down to him:

"Oh, Paul. I've kicked the bucket."

Paul promptly responded:

"It isn't as bad as that, Charlotte. You haven't kicked the bucket. You've just turned a little pail."

NATURALLY BEWILDERED

There's a mid-aged father in town who is smiling smugly into his mirror those mornings as he whittles his graying whiskers, and all because Carol, his teen-age daughter, is in a horrible state of confusion:

During the last year, Carol, in the ingenuous and impatient way of teen-agers, has more than implied to this father that he is old fashioned, square as a bear, drippy, and off the beam but def.

And then, the other evening, Father overheard Carol holding forth to one of her girl-friends:

"Do you know Sugar? You don't? Well, Sugar was my Girl Scout Counsellor, and she's right in the groove. She's one of these women who keeps on her toes, and knows us kids. Well—

"I almost died yesterday afternoon because Sugar told me she was going to a lecture at Wayne University, and who do you suppose was going to give that lecture? My goodness, my daaad!

"And I knew," Carol went on, "how solid she is and I know what a mouldy character Dad is, and anyway, this morning, Sugar told me that my dad's lecture was tops and that I'm so lucky to have a father who's as sharp as Hamp's Boogie!"

SWACKED!

Robert A. Raffin is back from a trip to New York that included a stroll through that perpendicular metropolis on Memorial Day when, naturally, the stores were shut as tight as an angry spinster's lips.

"As I was nearing a fashionable woman's Shoppe," he smiled, "I saw a typically curious New York crowd in front of the window. So I joined:

"The cause of the excitement was a fallen mannequin.

"She lay in deep disarray. Her arms, legs, and dress were very much awry, and her hair was down over her face. The whole effect was a rather ribald imitation of acute intoxication.

"She was wearing a rumpled brown creation, and a sign said the creation was called 'Chocolate Soda.'

"Which inspired one of the big-city wags to remark:

"Hmmmm. . . . Guess she had one too many!"

BREAD ON THE WATERS

Tommy Chisholm, who's 12 years old and naturally sports-minded, came into possession, for the afternoon, Saturday, of four passes to the Tiger-Yankee ball game.

He assembled three pals and to the park he went, only to learn, with lengthening face, that there was a service charge on each of those passes.

The four young fans went into a pants-searching huddle and

finally came up with just enough money to pay the service charges, leaving them so flat broke they faced an afternoon of no coke, no hot dogs, and, for that matter, walking home. However:

In they went, and the game began.

Pretty soon, a foul ball went up and back and down and—Tommy caught it.

Proud was Tommy of that performance. And then, a few rows ahead of him, he heard a wounded service man say to another: "I wish I'd gotten that ball."

Tommy bounced out of his seat and down to the soldier to say: "Hey, mister, you take this ball."

The veteran finally accepted it. In fact he wanted to pay for it, but Tommy wouldn't take the cash. However:

The pop-seller appeared out of somewhere and said to Tommy:

"That was a nice thing you did, kid. Have some cokes on me."

And then the hot-dog man came beaming along. Said he:

"That's the kind of kid I like. Have some hot-dogs."

And the man across the aisle, who'd taken this all in, leaned over, hurriedly shoved a dollar bill in Tommy's startled hand and saying, "Good goin' kid," he went back to watching a glorified game.

A PICTURE GALLERY?

It is being borne in upon us, particularly as we scan the advertising sections, that this oncoming Sunday is dedicated to a most peculiar character.

"Peculiar?" you inquire? Well—we know of no better adjective to describe a mere human being who is a grouchy bear, a haloed hero, a sleazy door mat, a strong sanctuary, a picture gallery, and a defunct dodo, all at the same time.

Nor do we think it is necessary to discuss any of the traits listed above, with the possible exception of statement that he is a picture gallery. Well—

He's all of that, is Dad because, deep in his mind he carries so many pictures; pictures of long-gone smallsters, grown big and sturdy now, or gone from this weary world, but, in those silent galleries of Dad's memory, smallsters still, with great eyes looking admiringly up at a man a bit embarrassed at the beauty of a youngster's adoration.

Pictures that come unbidden in the night, of laughing little faces, or the red of fever-flush; pictures that come in the bright of day, of confidences exchanged and little secrets shared. Ah well. . . .

Give good old Father what you will, come Sunday, but—

This is our great suspicion: Regardless of the value of the present he receives, it will be as nothing to what you, his children, have given him in the past—those pictures that go with him as he plods the path of glory and of sorrow that is life.

PERFECTLY LOGICAL

Mrs. Arthur Wyss, of Berkley, says that her family is accustomed to her father's wisecracks but "he ought to watch himself when strangers are around":

Recently, Mrs. Wyss' 21-month-old twins, Warren and Wallace, were spending two weeks with their grandparents near Mt. Clemens.

The boys haven't learned to talk yet, being content with the unintelligible sounds with which they seem to make each other understand. Well:

One day, Grandfather was busy at some chore on his small farm, accompanied by Warren and Wallie, who were conversing in their customary gibberish.

About then, a stranger, walking down the road, stopped and stared at the two. He got an expression of great curiosity on his face. He came closer, and stood at strict attention, listening to those two small boys chattering so strangely back and forth. Finally—

He signaled Grandfather to the fence and inquired:

"What language are those two kids talking?"

Grandfather looked greatly surprised. He asked: "Don't you know?" And when the stranger said he certainly did not know, Grandfather said:

"They're talking Chinese."

The stranger seemed considerably impressed. He demanded: "Where did they learn Chinese?"

Grandfather went back to his work, wafting as an answer, over his shoulder: "From a book."

A ROWBOAT AND THE REVEREND AL

Yesterday's mail brought us a copy of "The Universalist," a mimeographed news-sheet put out by the Rev. Albert Q. ("Just call me 'Al' ") Perry, in North Hatley, P.Q., Can.

On the page with the personals we grinned at an item reading:

"If you know of anyone who has lost a rowboat, kindly get in touch with the editor."

Yes, we grinned, and thought back about the Reverend Albert Q., a dynamic young man who exploded his first bomb during his first sermon by stating:

"My name is Perry. But I don't like to have folks call me 'Mr. Perry,' or 'Reverend Perry.' In fact—Just call me 'Al.' "

Whereupon, several elderly women, parishioners of many years' standing, and kneeling, almost keeled over. Their concept of religion included no idea of a minister who exhorted folks to "Just call me 'Al.' " However:

The Reverend Al was not taken aback at their astonishment. He just kept grinding along, day by day and week by week, spurting sparks like an emery wheel, sparks of energy and enthusiasm, to such an extent that most of the old-timers finally have compromised by calling him "Mister Al."

And this the old-line church-goers do in spite of many an unorthodox activity. For example:

When Stan Cuthbert, who runs the Hob Nob Restaurant, was heard moaning around the postoffice one Saturday afternoon that his short-order cook had just had all his teeth out and was hors de combat "and with a Saturday night trade coming up too," the Reverend Al inquired:

"How about me? I short-order-cooked my way partly through college."

That night, the Reverend Al was spatting out hamburgers and toasted cheese sandwiches until 3 a.m. Sunday, and bounced bright-eyed into church a few hours later to deliver a telling sermon based on a text, not from the Bible, but from Bing Crosby's song-hit, "Or Would You Rather Be a Fish?"

While we were in a cottage on Lake Massawippi last month, our nearest neighbors—half a mile away—were the Reverend Al, his shining wife, Irene; two small sons, Lewis and Bond, and one of the most courtly dogs we've ever met, Laddie.

One morning the Reverend Al, who'd been in the village to handle a Memorial Service, came putt-putting up to our dock in Joe Seguin's little inboard motorboat—it sputs once to the minute and makes three feet to the sput. He got out and hunched himself dejectedly on his heels:

"What you so blue about?" we demanded, and he replied:

"The parsonage is all painted, and so there's no excuse for 'Rene and me to stay in camp any longer. We've got to move down, tomorrow."

We took a look at the size of Joe Seguin's boat and began thinking about how many trips the Reverend Al would have to make to haul all his camping gear back to North Hatley.

We murmured sympathies, and after the Reverend Al had told us about a prodigious Northern pike that had practically chased him off the lake and into his tent, he departed; the motorboat trailing dejection and oil-smoke.

The next morning, with the sky a high blue and the lake a dream of idleness:

"Putt—Putt—Putt," and we knew the Reverend Al was coming down-lake with his first load of equipment.

In the motorboat where the Reverend Al and his wife, also a rolled up tent, on which hazardously perched the two small sons. The dog was up in the bow, soberly contemplating the water as it went past. But—

Behind the motorboat was a tow-line and to the tow-line was affixed a rowboat stacked so high with duffle it looked like a camel.

"Now where," we wondered, "did Al get that rowboat?"

The flotilla ambled in to our dock, Al shut off the motor and yelled: "Hey, do you happen to have a cigaret? 'Rene and I ran out. Otherwise we wouldn't have broken camp until this afternoon."

We had cigarets. Also the question: "Where'd that rowboat come from?"

"That's sort of interesting," said the Reverend Al, when he and Irene were smoking the smoke of the starved. "Last night I was wondering how I could get all my stuff down to the village in one trip. I certainly did wish I had another boat. But I didn't have. Well—

"That was just before I turned in, last night. This morning when the dawn woke me up, I looked out of the tent, and there was this rowboat, resting very gently against the beach."

He took another deep drag on his cigaret and stood up. His eyes twinkled.

"Sometimes things like that happen," said the Reverend Al.

THIS MATTER OF GREATNESS

We have an idea that the late Fielding H. Yost would have been astounded, could he have seen the reams of publicity and pictures accorded him at his death.

We rather think that "Hurry Up" Yost did not realize how famous he had become. But then—

Maybe a great many of the truly outstanding are too busy being themselves to take the time to measure how widely they are known. Take Babe Ruth, for example:

Roof Gilson says that one day when the Babe was at the peak of his fame; when the power of his bat had slammed his picture and name throughout the world, Gilson and Ruth were riding, in Ruth's car, over to a country club for a game of golf.

The car stopped at a traffic light, and an elderly man in an elderly car, glancing over, saw the Bambino and yelled:

"Hello, there, Babe."

"H'yareya," Ruth yelled back. "How things goin'?"

And, for the space of a red light, the two visited like old friends. Then, the Babe's 16-cylinder job purred away from the other car.

The Babe drove in silence for a thoughtful minute or two before he said to Gilson, in a puzzled way:

"I guess I must have the ugliest mug in the world. Everybody seems to know me!"

QUITE A DOG

Ruth Cunov set an interesting tempo for today's effort by flagging us down to assert:

"My mother read what you said about dogs that can tell what day of the week it is with considerable contempt because our dog, Sandy, not only can tell the day of the week, and the afternoon of the day, but he can tell whether it is five o'clock or six or seven. And—

"Now, Mr. Jackson, do not put on that skeptical expression, first because it is not warranted and second because it does not become you any more than the necktie you are wearing.

"Sandy could be expected to tell time to the hour because he is quite a remarkable dog—he thinks!

"I throw Sandy a rubber ball and a rubber bone at the same time, and his mouth is not large enough to hold both, and then I call: 'Sandy, bring them here!' And do you know what he does?

"He takes the bone in his mouth and golfs the ball to me."

JUST A QUIRK

We saw them coming down the street, a heavy, elderly woman, leaning on a cane, and a sprig of a granddaughter, starched and blithe and skipping.

They came to the curb and considered the red light against them. They waited quietly and the light went green.

Grandmother stepped down into the street with her right foot, and followed with her left. She did not use the cane.

The small girl had skittered several steps ahead. She turned, looked back, and instantly caught the fact that Grandmother was making it without the cane.

Then the small girl called something that the face-life-as-it-is-boys probably would call out and out escapism. She called:

"Now Granny, behave yourself and use your horse!"

And Granny, rather grumpily, began to use that cane.

NOTHIN' BUT A NOTHIN'

Friday, a salaried friend of ours had lunch with a man high up in the executive circles of one of the nation's big labor unions.

Our friend said, gloomily: "Well, if Congress lifts the lid on living costs, I know who's going to get it in the neck—it's white-collar guys like me."

The Union Big-Shot looked at our friend with obvious good will, shot through with pity. He answered:

"The trouble with folks like you, Joe, is that you're licked and don't know it—

"Oh, you white-collar guys are good fellows," he conceded, "but—you don't mean anything, politically, any more. You're just an echo from the dark ages of American individual initiative.

"You aren't organized, and so you can't put on any pressure, and so, of course, you're going to get it in the neck!"

BAUM IS BEFUDDLED

Baum fixed us with the eye of the Ancient Mariner and demanded: "Do I look like a guy the police would turn to for advice?"

Having known Baum for 31 years, we felt we could afford to be frank. We replied: "No, you don't."

"That's what I thought," said Baum, "and yet, this is what just happened:

"I was standing on the curb, minding my own affairs and a cigar that wasn't drawing well, when up pulls a police car and a big cop leans 'way over from under the wheel and yells:

" 'Hey, Mister. Where can I park?' "

Here Baum quiveringly lighted the duplicate of the cigar he'd mentioned. We asked: "What did you do?"

"When," said Baum, "I got over my paralysis, I looked around and there was a great sign reading 'No Parking,' so I pointed at it and told that cop: 'Park right by that sign.' And the cop looked mean and drove away and parked in an alley."

AFTERMATH OF A STORY

One of the easiest, and hardest, things Mrs. Jean McKenna, fourth grade teacher at the Cady School, Wayne, ever has had to do was to pass a pupil who was not even in class:

Three months ago, one of her students, Jimmy, nine years old, dropped out of school. He had been stricken with an incurable ailment.

Two weeks ago, Jimmy's mother made a call on Mrs. McKenna. She said:

"I wonder if you could do something for Jimmy? Could you make out his report card, showing he'd passed to the Fifth grade? It would make him so happy."

Mrs. McKenna said that she certainly could and would. So—

She made out that card promoting Jimmy to the Fifth grade.

It was one of his most treasured possessions when, just the other day, he was promoted to a grade far higher than the Fifth. . . .

PHYL'S EFFICIENT

There is considerable chuckling going on in one nearby community in which the becoming mother of three smallish sons, who's planning to take the two older boys on a trip pretty soon, began to wonder how she was going to get her baby-son cared for.

She was sure of one thing: Her husband couldn't do it.

Then she read, somewhere, of a service that supplies pro-tem mothers—women who move right in and, at a fee, take over the care and feeding of the infant.

The mother, we'll call her Phyl, phoned that service and outlined her problem to the lady-manager, who promptly came back with:

"Oh, we can take care of that situation perfectly. In fact, we have three pro-tem mothers who can move into your home, and whom I can recommend highly. One is 21; one is 30, and the other is 48. Just a moment and I will read you their qualifications."

Snapped Phyl: "To save time, just give me the qualifications of the one who's 48."

HAYDN HIT IT

Lou Tendler had undergone an extra hard day at the office, and with a good, if meatless, meal under his belt was settling down for a wee bit of an early evening cat-nap when into the living-room came daughter Judith, eight years old.

She went over to the piano and with considerable rooching around prepared to do her daily practicing.

She began fingering notes and Lou twitched his shoulders.

He opened his mouth to tell her to go away from there and let him have a little sleep, but he closed his mouth because, after all, Judith had to practice, and besides, Mrs. Lou had come in and Mrs. Lou has ideas about Judith's practicing or, for that matter, cat-naps after dinner.

It turned out that the rendition Judith was practicing was a soft and soothing something, with a nice little restful tune, and Lou so much relaxed that he went sound asleep, and then—WHAM!

Judith hit a chord so vibrant and resounding it bounced Lou out of his chair and into action. He snapped:

"For heaven's sake, do you have to make a noise like that?"

And Mrs. Lou began to laugh and laugh and laugh. Which did not improve Lou's disposition any. He groused:

"What's so funny?"

"That chord," said Mrs. Lou, "is part of the piece she's playing. Don't you know what it is?"

Lou, who knows no more about music than this tone-deaf column, said he didn't know what the tune was and Mrs. Lou explained:

"It's part of Haydn's Surprise Symphony. He put that loud chord in there to wake up the audience."

FOXING A WOLF

Marty is telling of a becoming young woman who just returned from San Francisco with what she believes is a cast-iron defense against would-be wolves.

The train hardly had started East before a young man with a roving eye followed his eye and sat down in the seat next Miss Detroiter.

"Lovely day, isn't it?" said he—and it may be that the tepidity of this opening salvo was what set her against him. Anyway:

Instead of giving him the Ice, or screaming for the conductor, or stamping on his instep, or anything of that sort, Miss Detroit leaned toward him, smiling rather vaguely, and cupped one hand around her ear.

She said: "Will you say that louder? I am a little deaf."

The young man got out of there as if bees were biting him. And that same technic worked five other times on her transcontinental trip. . . .

MEAN STORY

Thinking on collegiate subjects, there is Bud Nevin's story of along a story that simply goes to prove that we are a Mean Man, because when the physician told us about it, we actually grinned:

The physician came to our hospital room and said:

"There's a guy down the hall, a victim of pheasant-hunting."

"Shoot himself?" we inquired casually.

"Nope," said the physician, "it's more complicated than that.

"You see," he went on, "this guy is just nuts about pheasant hunting and pheasant eating. So, 'way back last spring he began shopping around for a better gun with which to shoot pheasants. Also he managed to black-market a lot of shotgun shells, and all summer he practiced up so he could be more certain of bagging pheasants when the season opened. Well—

"The season opened yesterday morning, and this guy went out in the fields, and in record time, he shot two swell pheasants. He got so excited about killing them, and how good they would taste that he blew the fuse on his stomach ulcer. He hemorrhaged so bad he's in the hospital and for the next six weeks they'll have him mostly on milk."

CHIDDEN

Thinking on collegiate subjects, there is Bud Nevin's story of the revenge wreaked by an elderly Latin professor that morning when his entire class admitted they were not prepared.

The professor looked down at them from the lofty heights of learning, and said:

"Class is dismissed. But may I ask you one favor, in view of the fact that other classes are being held in this building? As you walk down the corridor will you please refrain from braying?"

GRAMPAW KNEW

It was the first time the two small cousins ever had seen each other, or had ever been compared by their respective relatives—those from the country and those from the city.

The meeting was at an old home week on the family farm, and while everyone agreed the two little girls—Country Cousin and

City Cousin—looked a great deal alike, everyone was astounded when the two traipsed downstairs just before bedtime, each in a long white nightie, and each, we are surprised to learn, bare-footed.

"They're as much alike as two peas in a pod," gasped one auntie.

Another said, "You simply cannot tell them apart!"

"Mwumph," said Grampaw, with a snort. "Can't tell 'em apart? I'll show you how to tell 'em apart" and, turning to the two little girls he said:

"Hey, kids, look at the piggies!"

Country Cousin rushed and looked out the window. City Cousin looked at her toes. . . .

LEGACY

A widow here in town has rather somberly been reading a letter written her by her late husband. It says:

"My dear—It has been a sorrow to me that you have not shared my interest in rare books, but then, you have been very patient. You have not very often mentioned the amount I have spent on this hobby of mine.

"This little note will come to you after I have gone on, as I am convinced I am going.

"It is to thank you for having been so patient with my 'foolishness,' and to know that for once, you did open one of my choicest books."

This note was in a plain envelope in the husband's favorite rare edition, that was on the book-rack beside his easy chair.

It was sent her, without comment, by the bookstore man to whom she had hurriedly sold her husband's entire collection.

YOU'RE THE JUDGE

Dorothea Ryan, the Printers' Pet, came steaming over to our desk to demand: "Aren't you going to print that story? It's cute!"

"It's too obscure. Folks won't get it," we mumbled.

"It is not," asserted Miss Ryan. She turned to Cecil the Weecil.

"Cecil," she domineered, "you listen to this and see if you get it."

The Weecil got it. "There," snipped the Printers' Pet, "you see?" . . .

Mrs. Charlotte Wilson had written: "Took me a full second to figure out this one: Last night Don (who is now eight) picked up my list of groceries-to-be-bought and started reading the items. He went along nicely for a few. Then there was a pause and he said:

" 'One tick-tack-toe Rice.' "

WHAT A NIGHT AT NIAGARA FALLS

Jane says that she and her husband Ed began to be a little confused within a day or so after they became the hostess and host of Evelyn, a 15-year-old cousin who came on a visit from California.

Whether the celebrated climate had anything to do with it or not, Jane insists that Evelyn was certainly hard-boiled for a 15-year-old, or older.

All the attractions of Detroit left her politely yawning, and as the visit spun out, both Jane and Ed began to wonder if anything could crack Evelyn's glacial calm. Well, they know now.

One day Ed up and said: "Let's the three of us drive down to Niagara Falls."

And away they went, just like that, without a thought of reservations, or housing conditions, or honeymooners.

They reached the Falls at midnight, in the midst of a tremendous thunder storm. They took a quick look at the Falls between flashes of lightning, and started out to find a place to sleep. . . .

Jane and Ed decided after a couple dozen phone calls that things were sort of crowded in Niagara Falls, and it looked as if the three of them would snooze in the car, until—

"Ed thought about his lodge," Jane said, "and to it we went.

"After arriving, there were the usual mysterious hand-shakes, mystifying signs, and things of that sort, and then Ed said his brothers had fixed up a place for us. He even had the address with him. So—

"We drove over wet streets through the black and thunderous night, with lightning flashes bursting white around us, until we came to the address Ed had gotten from his brothers.

"It was a dark street 'way out in the suburbs, and the house looked like an old relic to us—what we could see of it—and then I saw too much of it, because the lightning flashed right then and clear across the second story of the house was a sign. It read:

" 'Funeral Parlors' "

Jane went on: "I was all for sleeping in the car, but that Evelyn said: 'This looks all right to me,' so I set my lips and Ed went up and knocked at the door.

"Evidently the Brothers had been working, because it opened immediately and there stood a grim-faced man and his equally grim-faced wife. They motioned us to come in, and we scurried in out of that gloomy rain.

"They took us up a dark stairway and a little hall and showed us two adjacent rooms. Then the grim-faced man had us sign our names and addresses on a sheet of paper and said:

" 'Ten dollars please. In advance. Just in case anything should happen during the night.' "

Jane thinks that maybe she was a little mean when she did not suggest that she and icy Evelyn double up in one room and let Ed take the other, but Jane just couldn't help waiting to see if Evelyn would make a first move.

Evelyn didn't. She went into the room with the single bed, and casually began to look around.

She strolled over to a clothes hamper and peeked into it.

She tried a closet door in the corner. It was locked.

Evelyn remarked: "I'd a little rather that door was open," and let it go at that.

Then Jane capitulated: "Wouldn't you rather bunk in with me and have Ed sleep in here?" she asked, and Evelyn replied: "By no means. I will be perfectly all right."

"Okay," said Jane, and glancing around the room, picked up a book. "Here," she said, "read yourself to sleep with this," and adding, "Good night," she went into the other room, feeling frankly pleased that Ed was on the premises.

Eventually daylight came. And:

Klop! Klop! Klop! came on the door of Jane's room.

It was Evelyn, a red-eyed Evelyn; a fully dressed Evelyn. "I'm ready to get out of here," she announced, and something about the shiver in her voice was the shiver of a 15-year-old girl rather than the icy Evelyn.

Jane and Ed got ready, while Evelyn waited in the hall. When they emerged, it was the 15-year-old Evelyn who waited for them. And an Evelyn with a wan twinkle in her eyes too.

"What a night," she gasped. "And I thought I was sophisticated! I was scared stiff," here she unleashed a little-girl giggle. "And, Jane, you didn't help much with that book of bedtime stories you handed me. It was a treatise on 'The Dissection and Embalming of the Human Anatomy.' "

TICKETED!

Wesley C. Redmond, with three share-riders doing some back-seat driving, was ambling through a sparsely built-up district of one of the suburbs when, out of nowhere came a Scout Car that nosed Redmond to the side of the road.

Out stepped some 16 stone of cop, with a beetled brow, a violations pad, and an eager yellow pencil.

"What gave you the idea you could drive like that?" demanded the cop of the chap-fallen Redmond.

Redmond gurgled: "What did I do?"

The officer heeded him not. He turned to those three share-riders, Harry Earley, Ed Hunter, and Ray Hopper. The officer fixed Hunter with a spearing eye and said:

"What do you think of this guy's driving?"

Hunter cleared his throat. He answered: "I hate to tell you this, Sir, but he just ran through a red light!"

"Soooo!" breathed the policeman, while Redmond slued his head around to stare at Hunter.

"I never did any such thing and you know it," howled Redmond, and in the ensuing silence an acute ear could have heard the rending ping! as the bonds of friendship snapped.

The officer had turned to Earley, inquiring:

"Do you think this guy is a good driver?"

"Officer," Earley responded earnestly, "if my car wasn't broken, and if I didn't have to get to work, I wouldn't dare ride with him."

"Soooo!" observed the policeman, and Hopper came in with:

"Every time he drives I get a step nearer nervous prostration."

While Redmond tried to gather himself together, the officer wrote out a ticket. He shoved it at Redmond. He said:

"This will cost you $2." He paused. He said: "Oh, by the way, there's this, too," with which he produced an envelope he forced into Redmond's flaccid hand.

Redmond opened it: A "Happy Birthday" card for Redmond from his three back-seat pals. And by gosh, it was Redmond's birthday. Folded into the card were two $1 bills, contributed by Redmond's puckish playmates.

SHE WAS DELIGHTED

It was a quiet evening gathering of folks who had been married for at least 15 years.

And quite the normal gathering, too, because all the men had clubbed together at one end of the large living room, to talk about politics and prices and prospects and athletics and other such items of man-talk; while all the women were clustered at the other end of the room, talking about whatever women do talk about under such circumstances.

Suddenly, Joe got up, detached himself from his section, walked the length of the room and—kissed his wife.

Mrs. Joe stared up at him and asked: "Are you leaving now?"

"No," said Joe.

"Then," quizzed Mrs. Joe, "why did you kiss me?"

"Just because I wanted to," said Joe stoutly.

Mrs. Joe's eyes grew round and large and luminous. She said:

"Why, that is the nicest thing that has happened to me in years! I thought I'd come to that stage in matrimony where a wife gets kissed by her husband only when he is leaving the house, or coming home."

THEY ARE INCLUDED

There be those among church attendees who sort of rooch around in their Sunday morning seats, if the minister has a long list of advance church notices, which he proceeds to read.

We've been inclined to suspect that some parsons are not particularly allergic to this practice.

Then comes this one about the Rev. Myron R. Bunnell, of the Greenfield Congregational Church:

Last Sunday he had a tremendous list of events-for-the-coming-week, including Boy Scouts, Brownies, Church Council, Women's Associations, et al.

When he'd gotten, rather breathlessly, through Wednesday of the oncoming week, he paused, inhaled deeply, and remarked:

"Incidentally, we have sermons on Sunday."

MORE SO

Ed says it took him a couple of days to get over the trembles following his week-end at a grim old house looking down on the Hudson River.

When he told some New York friends he was going there for a visit, the friends looked at each other and began hoisting eyebrows.

So obvious were their antics that finally Ed demanded:

"Say, is there something wrong with the folks who live in that house?"

"Oh, no, no," came the quick answer, "they are perfectly charming people. As you know, an advertising man and his wife. There's nothing wrong with them, but—why do they like to live in a haunted house?"

"A haunted house?" Ed echoed, somewhat emptily.

"That's the story," they told him. "Folks who have spent week-ends there insist there are strange noises from the basement. Either that house is haunted, or something is chained up down there. . . . Something the guests never see."

"Phooey," observed Ed, but in rather a deflated voice.

So he went to that house for the week-end: Charming host and hostess; a group of delightful guests; a made-over mansion, running back in history to the Revolution.

Everything up-to-the-instant in appointments, Ed thought to himself as he dressed for dinner. What's all this talk about ghosts?

Dinner time began with sprightly tongue-loosening cocktails. The dining room table glinted with the sheen of costly linen and silver.

Cat-footed servants did more than stand and wait. And the conversation, well, Ed insists he sensed a note of hysteria in it. As if everyone in that room was waiting for something weird to happen —perhaps not until the traditional hour of midnight, but—for something to happen. And then:

From somewhere downstairs came thumpings and bumpings, and what could have been the rattling of chains, and, most distinctly, a strange, muted sort of wailing.

The host, from his chair at the head of the table, looked down at the hostess. He glanced at the guests. Without saying a word he got up, hitched his faultlessly-fitting dinner jacket the tighter around his shoulders and walked out of the room.

The hostess chattered pleasantly on. The guests tried to play up. Even then there was a definite, if muffled, thud, thud, thud, in the basement, and again that wail, ending up a strangled sound.

It was perhaps five minutes later that the host came in again.

He slid unobtrusively into his place. Ed noticed, however, that his breathing was carefully controlled, that a lock of hair was out of place, that there was a cobweb on his left shoulder and that—could it be?—well, on his right wrist started a red line—like a deep scratch, that disappeared under his right cuff.

Also, Ed noticed, as did every other guest at the table, that at a moment when everyone was hurriedly talking at once, he glanced at the hostess, she raised her eyebrows faintly, and the host lifted his shoulders in the vaguest hint of a hopeless shrug.

Throughout the rest of the week-end, Ed and the other guests waited for something more to happen. And they certainly kept their doors tight-locked at night but—nothing else out of the ordinary did happen. Not a thing.

JUST FEMININE

The other day, on the radio, we mentioned the fact that the father of a six-year-old boy never is sure whether he is talking to a sensible small human, or to a P-40.

So Judy's father says boys have no corner on being unexpected.

Last week-end, at the finish of a day during which seven-year-old Judy had played baseball so diligently, and ineptly, she'd acquired a lump on her shin and had lost a baby tooth, and came home asserting she just had to have a catcher's glove—

That very evening at dinner, small Judy lowered her fork and stared fixedly at her father and inquired in a tone slightly lispy from the absented front tooth:

"Daddy, when are you going to buy me an evening gown?"

JOURNEY INTO THE SUBCONSCIOUS

To many, the oncoming item may seem obscure, but we'll bet it will be clear enough to many a mother (and father) of small children.

We're referring to the journey into the subconscious about which Arthur reported Monday morning:

"About 5 a.m.," said he, "daughter Susan, who's two, began

talking in her sleep. Her voice finally came up, and she started repeating:

" 'I don't want any more; I don't want any more.'

"I was just going to get up and wake her up to stop her, when her mother spoke up. She said, in a weary, a resigned voice:

" 'All right. Just finish your milk.'

"And Susan said, 'Yes, Mother,' and stopped talking, and so did her mother—who had been sound asleep all the time."

SPEED AND MORE?

Bud Nevin got to talking about the celerity with which houses are going to be built when Production really goes into high gear.

He painted a pretty vivid picture, although we suspect he dipped his brush in sarcasm.

"Why," he declared, "they'll be building homes so fast that they'll start one early morning, and by the next afternoon, they'll be throwing the tenant out for non-payment of rent!"

ANSWERED

John Wilton hurriedly got on the phone, smoothed the smirk from his face, and reported an incident of the other evening, when he was one of a group in a home in Detroit that included an Incurable Optimist.

This gentleman had been listening to the gloomy and dour predictions about what must come upon our country before any balance can be achieved. Listening, and getting more and more restless.

At last he had his chance. He went right to work, asserting that any ills we have noticed in the body politic and social aren't severe at all. Just a rash, as it were.

Having taken off from this platform he soared high in the thin blue ether of optimism, waggling his jaw and his wings to such an extent that a couple of those present began looking at the little clock on the wall above his head. It said two minutes to two, which is a little late, even for an optimist.

But he went on, to finish up with the statement:

"In fact, this great country of ours is perfectly sound and all right."

And the clock on the wall suddenly flopped a door open, a bird poked its head out and said: "Coo-coo, Coo-coo."

AS IT LOOKS TO A PRINCIPAL

Our chair creaked considerably as we read and re-read a note that came to us from the principal of one of the huger high schools in this area.

Is his the right attitude, or the wrong? And who are we to judge? That's the reader's right.

This is what he wrote:

"While laboring in the garage over the week-end, I had what seemed to me (and for me) a reasonably bright thought. It is that—

"Teaching what is known as citizenship to high school pupils these days is largely a matter of teaching them not to act like adults."

GITTA HOSS

We are so prone to take things for granted. Even such miracles as sunshine and growing things and health. So it's no wonder we take the automobile for granted. But—

Think of the genius it took, to weld a man with two legs and two arms into easy control of the power that is under the hood of a car! Nor was it always so.

We know a man who once sprained his ankle driving a car:

It was, as he tells it, back around 1904. He had a benzine buggy equipped, not with a steering wheel, but with a steering handle you swung from left to right. . . . One day, the front wheels hit an unexpected rock, the handle caught him in his belt, tossing him out of the car and into a sprained ankle.

Which somehow takes us back to one of the first automobile jokes. About the French-Canadian who was driving his plodding dobbin along the road, when a car pushed its nose around a curve.

Forthwith, the horse practically took wings. So abruptly that he landed the Frenchman flat in the road.

He sat up and surveyed his horse that, tail over the dash-board, was still going across the fields. Then he shook his fist at the automobile, which had dutifully stopped.

He yelled:

"Come on, you dam gasolin'. She's gone!"

'JUST LIKE A . . .'

Thelma Groom, of Roseville, chanced to be on a street car when on clambered a married twain she has known for many years—

So many years, in fact, that she can remember when they were both slender and svelte. Which isn't the situation any more because, even as the years have broadened their vision, it has broadened their understanding and undersitting, until either husband or wife is one of those DSR distresses, a three-quarter seater.

Both husband and wife headed for a vacant two-person side-seat.

Wifie slid in first. Hubbie took what was left, and, to be frank about it, hung over considerably. So much so that after some squishing and rooching around, he was heard to say, in far too loud a voice:

"Maw, tomorrow you start dietin'."

THE ALICE

The Alice, having parked most of her punctuation marks in the corridor, came breathlessly in and:

"Mr. Jackson," she said, "I am delighted to learn that you are allergic to the dimpled knees of high school drum majorettes. I am so excited I am thinking of proposing to have you put on the committee to select Miss Michigan and maybe Miss America because it looks to me as if you have the detached viewpoint that's needed to be a judge in the jungle of pulchritudinity but how would you like to be a judge in the contest which I am personally sponsoring which is this year's Miss Demeanor?"

HE WANTED SOME SLEEP

Miss Leslie Weary, one of Eastern Air Lines' reservation agents, looked mildly bemused around midnight the other night when she answered a long distance call from Cleveland.

Said the man's excited voice at the line's end:

"I want to find out if I can get a reservation on your plane from Detroit to Cleveland tomorrow morning at 9:30."

"Did you say from Detroit to Cleveland?" Miss Weary repeated, signaling John A. Grandland, city traffic manager, that something must be amiss.

"That's what I said, Detroit to Cleveland," the man's voice was firm.

"But you are in Cleveland," Miss Weary tactfully pointed out.

"Lady," came a Niagara of words from Cleveland, "here's the situation:

"I got into Cleveland early this evening, and I have a big business deal on at 11 o'clock tomorrow morning, and to put it over I've gotta getta good night's rest but—

"I can't get a room in a hotel in Cleveland, and I am not going to sleep in a park. Not me. I got it all fixed up:

"I've bought me a train ticket to Detroit, and got me a Pullman berth, so I am going to get on the train and sleep to Detroit, and then catch a plane back to Cleveland for my deal. Can Eastern Air Lines give me that reservation?"

Eastern could, and did.

FOR ALL THE UNFORTUNATES

Mrs. Sherely Phelps was walking through the beauty of the

afternoon in the quiet of Forest Lawn Cemetery, thinking of how true it is that a cemetery, when sorrow has dulled, can be a place of peace.

In the distance she noticed a hulking man, standing motionless, staring down at something.

As she drew nearer, she wondered if that man might be a prize-fighter, perhaps:

Above rough shoes and rough trousers he wore a black turtle-neck sweater. His jaw jutted in the peculiarly truculent way in which a heavy jaw can jut when its owner has a cap crammed down on his head.

Mrs. Phelps thought of passing this character rather hurriedly. But she did not.

He turned, at her footsteps and said:

"So this is the grave of little Sandra Dildine—a game little kid, was Sandra."

He paused and swallowed, and groped his way forward verbally as do those to whom actions come more easily than words:

"I come out here just to see her grave, and yet somethin' more than her grave. Because she wasn't just one poor kid buckin' a game she couldn't beat. She was all the poor kids who can't beat the game. The ones that get noticed and the ones that don't. . . . Even the kids that grow up and still can't beat the game." He stopped speaking. He added, with a rising inflection:

"I just hope nobody'll think I'm a thief if I take a carnation off'n her grave, to put in my Bible?"

"I'm sure no one would," Mrs. Phelps answered and paid him the tribute of walking quietly away. . . .

HARDLY AN ECHO

If you remember the big-businessman who went back to his farm boyhood to describe how busy he was by saying: "I had to put on the sideboards today," well—

John Penny is in with an observation: "It's odd how, under the stress of excitement or something, the unexpected will pop out of the subconscious:

"I wear glasses, but I didn't blame them when I got in a mild automobile accident the other day. . . . Nothing serious, but I was to blame, as the middle-aged woman who was driving the other car certainly brought out with a remark that sparked across the decades. She blazed at me:

" 'You got four eyes and still can't see!'

"Oddly enough," Penny went on, "the minute she'd said that she started at me and said, 'Oh, my goodness!' and in no time we were both smiling."

SENSIBLE, AT THAT

Mrs. John J. Spencer, noticing the picture of a benzine buggy of such an early vintage it didn't even have a windshield, took pen in hand:

"That motor buggy reminded me of a remark my great-grandmother made during her first ride in one:

"It was a buggy, as I said, without a windshield. Back in the days when the hat was tied on with a veil. After a quarter of a mile or so of (literally) breath-taking speed, Grandma consoled us by saying: 'Well, anyway, we'll have the wind in our backs going home.' "

ENCLOSED WITH THE BILL

The board of trustees of a church that is in the building stage felt that the legal work should be done by a good law firm, even though the charges might be higher than the board cared to face.

So it was to one of the city's top-flight firms that the board took the legal angles of the construction of the new edifice.

The bill arrived the other day and was opened at a meeting of the trustees. And the treasurer, with the eye a church treasurer always has for costs, whistled plaintively at the statement:

"To legal services, $82.50."

Then the treasurer picked something out of the envelope that had contained this charge—two somethings, in fact.

One was a note from the law firm's senior partner, reading bruskly: "I trust the enclosed will be of some use in your worthy undertaking."

The "enclosed" was that lawyer's personal check for $100.

JUST KEEP CALM!

Maybe it is because Mary is a widow who has done a successful job of bringing up two children, that folks in her neighborhood so often turn to her when they're in distress.

Mary doesn't get excited. Mary has the level-head. Mary seems always to know exactly what to do. . . .

Friday morning, Mary's phone dingled, and there was Eileen on the wire:

"Mary," she gasped, "I'm in an awful puzzle. I just don't know what to do. It's like this:

"I'm invited to Edith Spick's shower for Hazel Dinglehoofer, this afternoon but—I'm not invited to the Dinglehoofer wedding, so I don't know whether I should go to that shower. I've been fretting about it for two days, and I know you can tell me—"

"Now, now," came Mary's cheery voice. "Just hold everything, Eileen. Don't get all nervous and wrought up. Everything is perfectly all right. That shower was yesterday."

JOE'D BEEN THERE BEFORE

Mark the Lark has an attorney friend who's just back from a reunion. This attorney had a few well-chosen words to emit about reunions in general and that one in particular. Said he:

"I don't know why it is that my class reunions, anyway, start right out with some drinking, and then the gents begin to tell about how successful they've been. Well—

"Our gang got together, and immediately there were inquiries about Joe. Where was Joe? How could they have a reunion without Joe? Hadn't Joe promised to come?

"From which you can gather that Joe had been a spark-plug back in college days. We'd looked forward to seeing him, and, for that matter, hearing him, because:

"Joe's the kind of chap who always has a keen remark with which to tonsure the crown of wild-haired conversation.

"Right when the wailing about Joe was at its peak, a messenger came tearing in and delivered a telegram to our president. He opened it. He read it to himself. Then he read it out loud. It said:

" 'Delay all success stories three hours. I will be late.—Joe'."

TOO ACCURATE?

There's still some sniggering among the few sprightly souls who attended a particularly stuffy banquet the other evening.

At the speakers' table sat a row of white-tied oldsters, looking oddly reminiscent of mummies, embalmed, as it were, in the clear consciousness of their own importance.

When the toastmaster got up to start the speeches, he said, in a cathedral tone:

"Ladies and gentlemen and extinguished guests."

WHAT DID IT

One of the most brilliant—and alcoholic—men in town hasn't had a drink for a month and the reasons behind this self-imposed drouth might be interesting:

This man—we'll merely call him Joe—has a high opinion of his own brilliance and he has believed that his brilliance was enhanced by the application of a whole parade of cocktails, high balls or what-have-you.

About a month ago he was at dinner, and well overboard.

His partner was a woman of sprightly wit. Somehow the two of them got to thinking up wee-bit jingles, you know, the Pohems, and suddenly, the woman said to Joe:

"Here's one that fits you: When you're tight, you're trite!"

Joe's face went blank as he demanded: "Is that just a jingle, or do you mean it?"

She answered: "To tell you the truth, the minute you have a few drinks your brilliance leaves you. You get to be both trite and a terrible bore."

Joe blinked three times. He hasn't had a drink since.

PSYCHOLOGY

By the time Mamie arrived at two years old and could not say a single word, not a thing but "allie, allie, allie," over and over again, her mother began to fret. (Or so Alcib reports.)

Mother aired her worries to most of the mothers in the neighborhood, including Estelle, who is a very modern mother indeed.

She has taken courses in child psychology and that sort of thing, and the proof of the pudding is that her two and a half-year-old son, Sammy, can speak as meticulously as a radio announcer.

Estelle had a Big Idea. She suggested that Sammy go over and play with Little Mamie for a livelong day. Maybe Mamie, inspired by Sammy's vocabulary, would get over that eternally repeated "allie, allie, allie."

So this meeting of Sammy and Mamie was accomplished, and together they played, and Mamie's mother was delighted at the interest Mamie showed in the way Sammy could juggle the President's English.

However, she had to admit the next morning, that Mamie had picked up no words at all. She was still saying "allie, allie, allie" to everybody. About nine o'clock, Estelle, the efficient, called up to say:

"I think something must have gone wrong. Sammy won't say anything but 'allie, allie, allie'."

THROUGH THE YEARS

Mrs. Burt was sitting on the porch with a portly, elderly friend of hers when abruptly the friend, beaming through her glasses said:

"For goodness sake! Look at that!"

Mrs. Burt looked and saw, coming slowly along the sidewalk, a young man and a young woman.

They were holding hands—her left hand and his right. And he, with the other hand, was studiously guiding the baby carriage preceding them.

Mrs. Burt's friend chuckled.

"I never saw anyone like them," she said, and explained:

"I remember the day they started from their side-by-side houses, right in this block, for kindergarten. They went with their mothers, and those two were holding hands.

"And I remember the day they started out for the first grade. They were holding hands.

"And I remember when they came home from graduating from high school, in their mortar-boards and gowns. They were holding hands.

"And I remember the day he left for the Army. They walked down this same street, holding hands.

"And today," said Mrs. Burt's friend, "is the very first day they have taken their baby out for a walk and there they are—holding hands!"

HE EARNED IT?

The other evening, Bob, a 20-year-old veteran of the Battle of Europe, who still feels twinges from the wound in his thigh, threw an Open House for his age-bracket in the community where he lives.

Somewhere along in the party, Bill, Bob's 17-year-old brother, managed to cut his finger slightly, opening a coke bottle.

Ensued some discussion about First Aid, during which one of

the girls advocated cold water and a bandage, so there was an adjournment toward the kitchen, but Bob said:

"You just wait a minute, Bill, I've got just the thing for a wound like that."

With which he hurried upstairs, to come very soberly down a few moments later and invest Bill with his Purple Heart . . .

OF COURSE SHE WAS

You might care to consider a recent experience in the life of Cousin May, 80 years old, delicate and aristocratic:

Her niece had taken her to a concert and, on the way home, something went wrong with the car.

Niece got out and wondered what to do.

Cousin May sat calmly in the front passenger seat and looked patrician. Then:

Up boiled a car. Out bounced a man. He started toward Niece's auto, reversed his field, grabbed a package from the seat of his car and brought it with him.

"Trouble?" he demanded of Niece, and when she said a woeful "Yes," he snapped: "I'll see what I c'n do . . . Pardon my breath!"

He started for the hood of the car. He paused, squinted at Niece and shook his head. He spotted Cousin May. He studied her and deposited his package in her lap. He went to work. He repaired the carburetor, breathing the while, highly alcoholic fumes.

"There," said he, "fixed."

He retrieved the package from Cousin May's placid lap. He said: "Lady, you know wha's in th' package? Three quartsa likker. Knew I could trust 'em with you."

Cousin May responded, icily: "Sir, I am insulted."

POLICE BUSINESS

Ep the Epicure went over to the Petoskey station to get his annual, and belated, dog license.

As he was filling out the form and chatting with the pleasant, roly-poly officer behind the desk, the phone rang.

The officer scooped up the receiver and said, in a hard, official voice: "Number Ten."

Thereafter, while Ep's eyebrows slowly climbed the steep ascent of his forehead, the officer went on:

"What was that you said? Your dog? . . . Somebody gave him to you? . . . You want us to come and get him? . . . Oh, you don't? You want to keep him? . . . Aw, well, lady, we couldn't do that. No, we couldn't.

"I tell you what, lady. You give him a piece of candy, or maybe an ice cream cone. He'll be all right in a couple of days. . . . No, lady, we positively cannot come, under those circumstances."

The officer pronged the phone and said in a somewhat stifled tone:

"Now, what do you think that was? It was a woman, and night before last somebody gave her a dog and she wants the police to come over and do something about what's happened since yesterday, because—

"Yesterday she gave the dog a bath and she says that now the dog is mad at her!"

THE CARTOONIST

The cartoonist has a quaint way of ascertaining the state of health of his friends. He approaches each and inquires:

"How are you today? Are you in the pink or in the punk?"

DIFFERENT NOW

Mrs. EGW was riding the partly filled bus, and rather admiring the deeply tanned neck of the boy, maybe 12 years old, in the seat ahead of her.

At the next stop, this youngster suddenly came to life as another lad in that age-bracket stepped aboard. "Hi, Billy," he called, and Billy came back down the aisle to drop into the seat beside him, saying, as he did so: "Haven't seen you since school quit, Sam."

Then came the following conversation:

Sam—No. I been pretty busy. Been to camp for two weeks. Would have stayed longer but Dad has had to be off on strikes and that made him sorta short of money. Know what's next, though? Dad and Mom are going to take me to Put-in-Bay. How you like my tan?

Billy—Swell. I'd like to get a tan like that too but Maw, she keeps me dressed up all the time; tells me she never knows when her club friends are goin' to drop in; she would be ashamed if I was dirty.

Sam—Heck! Club women get dirty, too. How can they clean house and wash and cook and everything if they don't get dirty? . . . you been playin' ball much?

Billy—Not much, now. I listen to the games on the radio. One time my own mother got me a ball and bat. Daddy and I went out after supper every night and he called me his little Babe Ruth. We had lots of fun; we broke the cellar window. My own mother only laughed.

Sam—Where's your own mother now?

Billy—She died. I have a new Maw.

Sam—Aw . . . Say! Tell you what. You come over to our house. Dad loves kids. We c'n play ball, an' my Mom, she always has left-over pie-crust tarts for the kids.

Billy—Thanks, Sam, but—I guess I hadn't better . . .

ONE WOMAN'S VIEW

The News carried a piece the other day to the effect that around 250,000 voters were likely to lose their vote this coming November, chiefly, as far as we could gather, through disinterest. Well—

Mrs. Ollie Boehm, vice-president of the League of Women Voters of Metropolitan Detroit, sent out a circular letter inviting women to join that organization, which has as its prime purpose the educating of voters—

You know—bringing the issues clearly before them, and arranging meetings at which questions can be asked of various candidates.

Among the replies came one that included a dollar bill.

It was written by a woman who said, "I am a Swiss, and I am not an American citizen yet, although I am going to be, but I think you are doing a very fine work, and I would like to contribute this dollar. As a Swiss, I know that democracy can be kept alive only if everyone does his share."

Mrs. Boehm was impressed. She looked up the League's constitution and by-laws and found that provision had been made for associate members—women who were not citizens, but who would like, as it were, to "listen in."

She wrote this fact to Mrs. Swiss, who promptly joined.

Recently, the League arranged a meeting in the Thirteenth Congressional District, where Howard A. Coffin was the Republican candidate. He was on hand to speak, and to answer questions advanced by a committee from the League.

Mrs. Boehm was at the door before the meeting started, and was amazed at the appearance of a woman with whom she was not acquainted.

The woman looked as if she had been badly beaten up. There were bruises and bandages on her face; she was limping, and one arm was in a sling.

She turned out to be Mrs. Swiss, who explained:

"I was hit by a taxicab last evening, and my doctor told me I was so badly hurt I had to go to bed and stay there for at least a week. Well," and her chin lifted determinedly, "I told him I was going to be too busy this afternoon to be in bed, because I had to be here to take my little part in democracy in action."

SHE HAD

The only other time we've ever heard of Ty Tyson being left

(temporarily) tongue-tied was when he was doing some crowd-interviewing in front of the Majestic Building (about where the paper bag once stood).

His vis-a-vis was a serious-faced elderly lady who earnestly answered each of Ty's questions, but produced nothing but "Yes" or "No".

Ty, fumbling around for a subject that might make her a bit more vocal, noticed her wedding ring and said:

"How long have you been married, Lady?"

"Thirty-five years," she said.

"And," said Ty, hopefully, with another look at the really beautiful wedding ring, "have you kept anything to remember your wedding day by?"

"Yes," said she.

"What?" pried Ty.

"My husband," said she.

SEMI-SAMARITAN

For 16 years, Bob has been driving a company car, with the name of the company emblazoned on its side, and has rigorously obeyed the company rule of "No riders." But—

During a recent afternoon rainstorm, he saw two elderly women standing in a bus stop, getting thoroughly drenched. And one of the women looked like his mother, so:

Bob stopped and offered the two a lift, which they accepted, in silence.

Fifteen blocks later, one of them said: "This is where we get out," and out they got, without benefit of a "Thank you," and Bob went about his work.

When he reached the office, the auditor wanted to see him, and the auditor said: "You know it is against the rules to give anyone a lift in a company car, and yet, that's what you did this afternoon."

Bob blinked, confessed his crime, and explained it. He couldn't help adding: "But how did you know?"

"Oh," said the auditor, "the women called up. They said they thought we ought to be told what our company cars are being used for."

WHAT A PASSENGER

Via Marion Bemis and Mrs. A. Bruce Knight comes a philosophical story dealing with Joseph Archibald Brown, the eminent house painter who, one of these recent balmy days, rested while trimming Mrs. Knight's house, and held converse with her.

Mrs. Knight was at the bottom of the ladder; Brown, at the top. Brown observed:

"Been thinkin' about John Dinglehoofer. Read his obituary in last night's paper. Made me think of the times I picked him up early part of the war as I was drivin' to work.

" 'John,' I said, drawing to the curb, 'you want a ride?'

" 'Always glad to ride with a gentleman,' John said, and jumped in and slammed the door so hard he broke the window.

" 'Gosh,' said John, 'Did I break that glass?'

" 'Nope,' I said. 'That's been broken a long time.' Well:

"The war was on, and it took me quite a lot of trouble to get a new glass, and the day it was installed, as I was driving along, there was Dinglehoofer at the curb.

"So," said Brown, "I called: 'Want a ride, John?'

" 'Always glad to ride with a gentleman,' John said, and jumped in and slammed the door so hard he broke the window.

" 'Gosh,' he said, 'did I break that glass?'

" 'Nope,' I said, 'I just haven't had time to get it fixed.' "

VIEWPOINTS

Additional proof that there are at least two points of view about anything (and usually a minimum of six) comes in an incident of the autumnal vacation taken by Captious Karl.

The man in charge of the horses at the riding center where Karl vacationed was a city product this year, not as well liked as Ab Junkins, the native who'd been on the job last year.

One day, Karl dropped down the road a bit to chin with Ab who, in the course of the conversation, inquired:

"How you like that feller they got in charge of the hosses?"

"I guess he knows his business," Karl answered, "but he's too formal."

"It ain't reely that," observed Ab. "It's just that he's a city feller, and you city fellers would rather have us natives around than the city fellers, because you think we're sorta dumb and you get fun out of laughin' at us, which is fine, because that's just the way us natives feel about you city fellers."

WHY SANTA WALKED OUT

As Mrs. Jay Jones and her small son were about to enter Littel's Children's Department Store in Redford, both of them stopped, because, by them hurried a Santa Claus.

"Where's Santa going?" the boy rather wailed, and, of course, his mother could not answer.

When they got inside the store, three women clerks were in a huddle, apparently talking something over, and looking at the door. Well—

Mrs. Jones did her shopping and, drawing her reluctant son by the hand, they walked out of the store. And then they saw Santa:

He was half in and half out of the back door of a car parked at the curb.

He was listening attentively to the wistful words being spoken by the pallid little cripple propped up on the back seat.

HOW MRS. BILL GOT THAT WAY

Mrs. Bill called her husband at the office, Monday morning. The moment Bill heard her voice, he cocked an ear, because Mrs. Bill is a placid, cheerful lady, a middle-of-the-road lady, but on this occasion wild excitement rode her over-tones.

"Bill," she gasped, "a friend of yours sent us a beautiful goose for Christmas dinner."

"Swell," gloated Bill, "and you'd better get it right over to the butcher and have it dressed."

"It is dressed," said Mrs. Bill, "but it still has the feathers on."

"Then get it over to the butcher," Bill ordered. "Taking the feathers off a goose is a terrible job."

"I," snapped Mrs. Bill, "should spend good money for anything like that. I'll do it myself!" with which she cradled the phone and Bill, shaking his head, went back to work . . .

When he opened the front door that evening, there sat Mrs. Bill in a chair in the corner of the living room. To his cheery "Hello," she gave him a level, morose glare and said not a word. She somehow gave the impression of a sulky puppy peering out from under a bureau.

But small daughter Margaret spoke. She said, tearfully:

"I do not know what is the matter with Mother. She won't speak to me."

"What happened?" puzzled Bill.

"I'd been out playing this afternoon," wailed Margaret, "and when I came in the whole house was full of little feathers, so I just said: 'Mother, what's in the air?' and Mother said: 'Shut up, you Brat!' "

THERE'S A DIFFERENCE

Cecil the Weecil speared us with an I've-got-a-joke eye and:

"Jack," said he, "which would you be more interested in: patrimony or matrimony?"

We walked carefully around that one before we decided to hedge by asking: "What's the essential difference?"

The Weecil had his mouth open but before he could speak, Peerless Pedro had the floor. Looking as prim as a parson at a beer party, Pedro explained:

"Patrimony is when you have large sums of money left you and matrimony is when you have large sums of money taken away from you."

HOMES ARE ALWAYS WORTH THE SAVING

The youngish man had the restless hands of the worried—hands that simply would not stay still. And restlessness seemed particularly out of place in his work blackened hands, coming on strong wrists from the sleeves of a well-worn leather jacket.

"My wife's going to divorce me," he said, "and I wondered if you could do anything about it." We slumped back in our chair and stared out at the late September sunshine and felt as hopelessly helpless as a man does feel when he is asked to play Jehovah in the life of someone else.

"She's left me," he went on, "and taken our little boy with her. She's goin' to divorce me."

We decided to be blunt. "Drink?" we demanded.

"No," his hands fumbled a cigaret from his pocket, "I don't drink much. It's . . . . gamblin'."

"O-o," we said.

"I'm 'way behind," he muttered. "And they're movin' in on me. I gotta sell my truck to pay those gamblers off. Can't you do something?"

We said: "This we can do: I can put you in touch with the man who, of all men in Detroit, knows men and women and matrimony—if you're willing to go to him and—tell the truth."

"I'll tell the truth," he promised, plucking lint from his trousers' leg. "I don't like gamblin' much. Or I didn't when I started. I just wasn't makin' enough to give my wife and kid what they ought to have had. I—"

"Hold it," we said and reached for the phone. We talked to Ralph.

"There's a young man over here who's afraid his wife's going to divorce him. Can I send him over?"

"Sure," Ralph answered in his voice of infinite patience, "I'll see what I can do. What is it? In-law trouble, drink, sex or money?"

"Gambling," we said.

"Probably pride," Ralph snorted. "Send him along . . ."

Two hours later our phone rang. "Jack," Ralph reported, "I think that fellow you sent over here will be okay—

"He's not a wrong guy. Just a chap who went a little off the beam—I'm going to talk to him and his wife tomorrow. She's coming to my office."

"Sorry to have troubled you," we regretted, "but that sort of thing isn't in our line."

"Shucks," came the infinitely patient voice, "you didn't trouble me . . . Homes are always worth saving."

Late the next afternoon, Ralph was on the phone again:

"Jack—that young fellow you sent over. I've just finished up talking to him and his wife.

"She's pretty bitter. Says he's been spending all his money on gambling. Says he gambles when he should be working.

"It looks to me like one of those things: That's the way she feels. But I got the idea she got ashamed of him because he wasn't making as much as three brothers-in-law she's got, and of course she thought he ought to be making more because she thinks he's a lot smarter than any of them.

"Maybe she let a little of that drop one time when she was mad. And he was in a state to pick it up because the Army turned him down because he's got asthma, and he felt sorry enough for himself so he was ready to make himself a hero by being a goat. Anyway:

"They're going to try married life again. I think they'll make it. I" (and here a chuckle) "I gave both of 'em holy hell!"

Last Saturday, the phone rang. A brisk voice said:

"I guess you don't remember me, but I'm the guy who was in last September when my wife left me. I just thought I'd tell you we had a swell Christmas . . . Thought you'd like to know I got those gamblers off my neck. I've been working on two jobs."

"Two jobs?" we puzzled.

"Yep," came that bright voice, "for the last three months—I got up at 5 in the morning, got home at 1 the next morning. That way, I got the dough, and paid off the gamblers, and had enough ahead so there were some little presents at Christmas for the kid, and the wife."

"Good going," was all we could think of saying.

"I've got to quit one of my two jobs, though," he added.

"Why?" we asked.

"Aw," he growled, "on account of my wife . . . She won't let me work so hard."

WHAT'S IN A CHAIR?

A week or so ago, the President's chair sprang a-leak or a-creak or something, so the President of that organization demanded service, and he got it.

The chair, via truck and manpower, was wheeled to the far recesses of the factory, and ended up in the carpenter shop, presided over by a man whose sense of humor is as dry as his sawdust.

This gent proceeded to repair the chair in jig-time, but it didn't get back to the President in jig-time:

Having fixed the chair, the carpenter began wondering how it would feel to be a Big Wheel. So he hauled the chair close to a table, and seated himself in the seat of the mighty.

He felt so prosperous about the whole thing that he decided to be an Executive and put his heels on the table. He did. He leaned prosperously back and broke the back of the chair . . .

CHIMPANZEES

Last week-end was, for us, wogged up by the number of folks who phoned in about whether or not they could actually think a minute into seconds, and come out with a minute's length of time.

Burt Thomas, however, before his departure for the hospital, passed on a bit of information.

"The way a lot of photographers count seconds when they have no stop-watch," said he, "is to say the seconds in chimpanzees."

"Huh?" we blinked, and Mr. Thomas accommodated with:

"They count seconds like this: One chimpanzee, two chimpanzees, three chimpanzees, and so on up to sixty chimpanzees."

"And when they get 60 chimpanzees," we demanded, "what do they do with 'em?"

"Send 'em to the zoo," snorted Mr. Thomas.

IN THE DAWN-WORLD

In that strange dawn-world in which small youngsters dwell, fact and fancy are so intermingled that it is hard, sometimes, even for the most perceptive parents to understand . . .

And this brings us to the remark made by small Mary at prayer-time the other evening: Something that, in a way, pushed back her mother's horizon:

Mary, with her eyes closed, went through the standard prayers, with many a request to bless Daddy, and Mummee, and Uncle Jim, and Aunt Margaret, and Mike (the gardener), and Wriggles (the dog) and—well, you know the list that little ones recite.

After Mary had finished, she remained with her eyes closed for a long half minute. Then her eyes opened dreamily and she said:

"Mummee, God yawned."

Her mother stared at her, temporized:

"Oh, you don't mean that. You mean you felt like yawning."

"No," Mary was most earnest about it. "God yawned. He told me he is so tired of blessing so many people."

WRONG PEW?

Bert Penny says that Louise still looks a little restless whenever anyone brings up her hospital experience:

Shortly after she was married, her husband came down with an acute appendix, and was whisked to the hospital.

Louise went along and, while he was in the operating room, she wandered restlessly around, looking for some place where she could smoke a cigaret.

Finally, she glanced through a door and saw a man puffing furiously so, in she went and quickly enkindled a cigaret.

It was hardly lighted before she noticed, through her daze of worry, several more men.

None seemed able to stand, or even sit, still. They paced up and down; they chain-smoked cigarets; they chewed their fingernails.

Louise joined them, pace for pace, cigaret for cigaret, nail-chew for nail-chew.

After a while a nurse appeared in the door and everyone stopped, like so many versions of Mrs. Lot.

Louise was first to react. She hurried to the nurse. She asked: "Any news?"

The nurse replied: "This is rather odd."

Then she added: "Do you really prefer to be in here with these expectant fathers?"

COMMERCIAL SENSE?

There be those who come into this world with what might be called Commercial Sense — the x-ray ability to see a dollar before it has developed. With which prelude:

Don Slutz has a friend down New York way whom we'll call Mac:

A few weeks ago Mac was driving through the upper end of Westchester County when he ran out of cigarets.

He stopped at a bit of a general store and was in the midst of his purchase when his eye lit on a small black elephant made of plastic.

Mac studied it as he paid for the cigarets. He asked:

"How much does that elephant cost?"

"Dollar'n a quarter," answered the storekeeper.

"How many have you?" inquired Mac.

The storekeeper stared at Mac. He said, off-hand:

"Oh, 30 or 40, I guess."

"I'll buy all you have," said Mac.

The storekeeper's eyebrows tried to meet his retreating hair. Meanwhile, he began squinting so carefully at Mac that he whisked out a well-wadded wallet.

That was proof enough of sanity for the storekeeper. He rustled around in the back room. In all, he had 60 of those little black plastic elephants.

Mac passed over $75 and the storekeeper nearly passed out . . .

Homeward hied Mac in high good humor. And this is what he did:

He put those elephants in small individual boxes and, getting a list of the names of the Republican chairmen in that part of the county, he sent each of them an elephant, with a note reading:

"Dear Sir: Here is something new in Republican elephants. You will notice that while most elephants have their trunks dejectedly a-dangle, the trunk on this elephant stands straight up—it is the Republican elephant Triumphant. If you do not want it for a mere $5, send it back at my expense."

At last report, no Triumphant elephant had been returned. And Mac's total was mounting past the $260 mark . . .

HARD TO BEAT

Willard Wolfe gives it as gospel fact, that the male students in a hilly college town in the South have quite a system for taking their dates, in automobiles, to campus doings, at a minimum cost.

While students are not allowed to have their own cars at that school, the frowning faculty relents enough to allow automobiles on dance nights. And this decision brought delight to two business men in the college town because they rented cars; you know the drive-yourself, pay-by-the-mile system.

These business men, however, are tremendously bothered by the scant amount of mileage run up by the students.

They have not yet found out that these young men, once they have a drive-yourself car out of sight of its garage, proceed to drive it backward, so the speedometer won't work.

Willard says it's quite an interesting sight, though, to watch one of those astute young men back his car up and down hill, to a sorority house, insert his date, and then back to the dance and back.

BOYS WILL BE . . .

Mrs. A. J. Kohler does not believe the returned GI would appreciate having his name used so we'll call him, with our normal originality, Joe.

Joe had been stationed in India, and supplemented his military activities with a deep study of that tumultuous country, its history, its customs, and religions.

He brought back with him numerous interesting relics, and so fluently and well did he talk about them that the pastor of his church asked him to lecture at an evening gathering.

Joe complied, to find an audience ranging from several Boy Scouts squirming on the front row, past teen-agers behind the Scouts, past mid-marrieds, to several Serious Souls at the back.

Things were made a trifle more complicated for Joe because the folding chairs holding the Boy Scouts were rickety. They creaked as the boys rooched around. Joe went ahead and, in the course of his talk, he passed out those relics, which the Scouts studied, and then handed to the others.

When Joe had finished, his souvenirs were in the hands of the most Serious Soul, who bore down upon him, thanked him for his lecture, and said:

"But there is one beautiful piece of wood among your relics that I simply do not understand about."

Joe looked at it and he didn't understand about it either, until he found out it was a slat from one of those rickety folding chairs that one of the Scouts had added.

SO MRS. EIGHTY-ODD HAD NO WHISKY SOUR

We have the assurance of Mrs. B'ham Bill that about the first thing Mrs. Eighty-Odd-years-old said she wanted when she reached the home of Mrs. Seventy-Odd-years-old for a visit, was a whisky sour.

This came as no great surprise to Mrs. Seventy-Odd because she knew that only recently, when Mrs. Eighty-Odd went to the David Whitney Building for some dental work, she made an excuse and slipped over to the Statler and drank a Martini. But—

Mrs. Seventy-Odd is not up on matters alcoholic, as we think will be apparent if we let her tell the rest of the story in her own words—words that also explain why Mrs. Eighty-Odd went whisky-sour-less:

"So, of course, I did not know how to make a whisky sour, so I went right over to Davey Jones' drug store because Mr. Jones knows everything. But—he did not seem to know how to make a whisky sour.

"Mr. Jones asked me why I didn't go to Mike's place across the street, and that really shocked me because in all my life I have never been in a saloon, but then, Mrs. Eighty-Odd was my guest and if she wanted a whisky sour I felt I should see that she had one, so I went over to that saloon and I was greatly surprised:

"There was no sawdust on the floor, and the people in there did not have on derby hats, leaning against a bar with their feet on a brass rail, and expectorating around half-smoked cigars into large cuspidors.

"Everything was bright and neat as a pin—as neat as the part in the hair of the charming young man behind the bar who looked very interested when I walked in, for some reason, and then he looked rather surprised, when I said to him:

" 'Can you make me a whisky sour?'

" 'Lady,' he said, 'I am an expert on whisky sours; er, do you want one?'

"So I explained about my eighty-odd-year-old house guest who wanted one, and I told him I'd like to have him make a whisky sour right away and wrap it up and I would take it home with me. But—

"He looked very shocked and he said he couldn't do that. He said:

" 'It is against the law to wrap up whisky sours and carry them away like that.'

"So I asked him if there wasn't any way that whisky sours could be taken out in conformity with the law, and he said:

" 'If you carry the whisky sour out in you, Lady, it's legal!' "